To Mother Mary,
a "legend in her own time".
Bob

ABORIGINAL MYTHS & LEGENDS

ABORIGINAL MYTHS & LEGENDS

Age-old Stories of the Australian Tribes

Selected by

ROLAND ROBINSON

With Illustrations by Roderick Shaw

PAUL HAMLYN

LONDON : NEW YORK : SYDNEY : TORONTO

Published in 1969 by
THE HAMLYN PUBLISHING GROUP LIMITED
London : New York : Sydney : Toronto
Hamlyn House, Feltham, Middlesex, England

© Roland Robinson

Designed in Australia by Roderick Shaw
Typeset in Baskerville by Harley & Jones, Sydney
Printed by Lee Fung Printing Co. Ltd, Hong Kong

FRONTISPIECE: WANDJINA, THE RAIN GIVER

Contents

Acknowledgments

Acknowledgments are gratefully made to R.H.Mathews for 'The Whale and the Native Bear', 'The Fish-People', 'Lake Boolaboolka', 'The Giant Tree', 'The Travellers', 'Why the Owl has Large Eyes', 'The Emu and the Crow', 'How the Kamilaroi Obtained Fire', and 'The Cave of Byama' from his *Folk-tales of the Aborigines*, also for 'The Seven Sisters'; to A.Oldfield for 'White Tribe and Black Tribe' from *Aborigines of Australia*; to R.M.Berndt for 'The Curlew and the Owl', published in *Mankind*, and to Ure Smith Pty Ltd for the same legend from *World of the First Australians*; to J.R.B.Love for 'The Tale of the Winking Owl', published in *Mankind*; to R.Brough Smyth for 'The First Men', 'The First Women', 'The Scattering of Mankind', and 'The Native Bear' from *The Aborigines of Victoria*; to Mrs K.Langloh Parker for 'The Bunyee Bunyee or Bunyip', 'Billai', 'Murgah Muggui', 'The Lyre Bird', and 'Yaraandoo' from *Woggheeguy*; to A.C.McDougall for 'Uli-tarra and his Warriors'; to *The Sydney Morning Herald* for 'The Platypus' and 'The Flowering Tea-Tree' by R.Robinson; to *Bank Notes* for 'The Old Man and the Rainbow-Snake' by R.Robinson; to Angus and Robertson for 'The Kangaroo-Man', 'The Porcupine Ejenak', 'The Wild Cherry Tree', and 'Under the She-oaks' from *Blackfeller Whitefeller* by R.Robinson; to G.Aistan for 'The Blood of Marindi', from *Savage Life in Central Australia*; and for the remainder of the material to *Legend and Dreaming* and *The Feathered Serpent*, published by Edwards and Shaw.

For Corlala and Buninjiwa

Adam and Eve
and the Dilly-bag

Some years ago, a man who used to catch snakes and young crocodiles for zoos asked me to go with him on a trip into the Northern Territory. He had to catch a lot of different kinds of snakes, goannas, tortoises and crocodiles, and wanted me to help him. The man's name was Eric Worrall. Since then, he has written many books on Australian wild life and now has a large reptile park near Gosford in New South Wales.

We made our camp on the Roper River, not far from the Elsey Homestead, where Mrs Aeneas Gunn once lived. Mrs Gunn wrote the books, *We of the Never-Never* and *The Little Black Princess*. And not far from where we were camped was a tribe of Aborigines.

We became friendly with these Aborigines. They belonged to the Djauan tribe, and they used to help us catch the various reptiles we wanted. We would wade with the Aborigines into a billabong. We would form a line across the billabong. Then we would keep diving and swimming under water, moving up the billabong looking for tortoises and water-snakes.

Sometimes we went out with the Aborigines when they were stalking and spearing kangaroos, or we would go with some of the children after mussels and lily-bulbs, wading and feeling with our feet and hands for them in the deep mud of a billabong.

Quite often we would be invited down to their camp in the evenings to take part in their sing-songs and play-about corroborees. We would sit with them round the fire in a dry, sandy river bed under the paperbark trees. One man would be playing the drone-pipe, a length of hollow bamboo. Another man would be beating time with the song-sticks, other men would be quivering boomerangs together. We would be clapping our hands or beating our thighs in time with the rest while Jeemborala, the song-man, was singing.

Someone would nudge me in the ribs with an elbow. I would look around, and there, dancing behind me on the sand in the moonlight, would be the dancers, the children in the front line, behind them a line of older children, and behind them a line of grown-ups. Eric and I learned some of the songs and sang them with the others. Some nights the moon would set behind the paperbark trees before we said 'Bo-bo' (good-bye), and made our way back to our camp.

One day I was sitting with Jeemborala near a deep spring that had tall reeds and bulrushes growing round it. I had told him a story I had read about a girl called Nerida and a young man called Birwain. Nerida was forced to go down into a spring, like the one we were sitting beside, by a spirit who lived in the spring. Birwain tracked her to the spring and dived in after her. The spirit was angry and changed

9

Birwain into reeds and bulrushes. Then Nerida was changed into a water-lily that grows among the reeds.

Jeemborala said that Nerida was a 'water-lubra', a girl who lives in rivers and springs. He then told me a true story about a man who caught one of these 'water-lubras'. I wrote down this story which Jeemborala told me, and you will find it in this book.

Another Aboriginal friend of mine on the Roper River was the old man Goodoonoo. I used to ask Goodoonoo to tell me stories of how their world was made. I told Goodoonoo our story of Adam and Eve.

So that Goodoonoo would understand, I said that God made Adam and put him in a country called Eden. In Eden there was plenty of food wallaby, porcupine, possum, fish, duck, mussels, water-lilies and yams. But, I said, Adam was not happy. He just sat around the camp fire. He didn't want to go out hunting. And God knew what was the matter with him.

One day, when Adam was asleep, God came and took a rib out of Adam's side. Adam didn't wake up or feel anything. Then God sat down and made, out of Adam's rib, a lubra called Eve.

When Adam woke and saw Eve, he was happy. He wanted to go walkabout with her. 'Now,' he said, 'I have a mate to carry the dillybag and the coolamon. I can walk ahead with just my spears to carry, and keep a look out for kangaroos.'

Goodoonoo said that his tribe had stories like 'Adam and Eve and the Dillybag'. He said that their stories were about 'The Dreamtime', which means, 'In the Beginning', when the world was made. He then told me a story about an old man, like God,

COOLAMON AND DILLY-BAG

called Nagacork, about the Rainbow-Snake and a big flood. I wrote this story down as Goodoonoo told it to me, and you will find it in this book also.

When the time came at last for Eric and me to leave our Aboriginal friends on the Roper River, I had filled many note-books with their stories.

Since the Aborigines could not write down their stories, you may wonder how they can remember them all; you may wonder if they are true, or if they are just made-up stories. Well, one Aboriginal, who watched me writing down a story as he told it to me, could not understand why I could not carry the story in my head.

He said to me, 'My mother told me this story, and she got it from her mother, and so on right back to the "Dreamtime". The old people, they couldn't read or write,

TOTEMIC BURIAL POLES

but they had their stories in their mouths, and they had them in their hands. They danced and they sang all their stories.'

Yes, these 'Dreamtime' stories of the Aborigines have been told round the camp-fires for thousands of years. They have been danced and sung for thousands of years by the Aborigines in their corroborees.

And are they true, or made-up stories? They are as true as our story of Adam and Eve. They are so old and true that they tell of a time when the present deserts of Central Australia were so lush and fertile that huge prehistoric animals lived there in the forests and swamps.

An explorer and scientist, J. W. Gregory, was told an Aboriginal story of this time in Central Australia. He travelled to the place in the story, and there found the bones of these huge animals. A complete skeleton of one of the animals is in the Adelaide Museum. It is called a Diprotodon.

These stories are so old that they tell of a time when Australia was joined to New Guinea. Although we believe that the Aborigines have been in Australia for between 30,000 to 60,000 years, they have stories of their coming to Australia. One of these stories in this book is 'The Whale and the Native Bear'.

And where did the Aborigines come from? We think they came from India and Ceylon and Asia. We think that they followed the land masses and islands down to Australia.

These stories are something like the stories in the Bible. They are like the fables of Aesop, or the stories by the Grimm brothers, or the Greek myths. They are like all

11

stories from all over the world of the time of 'In the Beginning'. They not only tell of how the Aborigines' world was made, they often speak of the Aborigines' God.

When the white man came to Australia, there were some 500 different tribes living here. And so the Aborigines have different names for God. You will find their God in these stories. Sometimes he is called Pund-jel, or Byama, or Nagacork, but he

NAGACORK AND KUNMANGGUR, CREATOR

is really the same God. He helps and looks after the Aborigines, and, like our God, he punishes them when they do not live by, and carry out his laws.

The Aborigines believe in, as we do, the spirit, and a life after we die. The story in this book called 'The Travellers' tells of the journey which a good spirit makes to the Aborigines' heaven, and it also tells of the journey a bad spirit must make, and of what happens to him in the end.

Some of you must have read fairy stories and fables in which the animals and birds talk like human beings. You will find this happening all the time in Aboriginal stories. In fact, the Aborigines will tell you that in the Dreamtime, all the animals, birds, reptiles, the sun, the moon, and the stars, were all men and women. You will find plenty of stories in this book telling you how men and women changed into animals and birds, the stars and the moon.

Every tribal Aboriginal has what we call a totem. This could be a kangaroo, or an emu, or a goanna, or a fish. The Aboriginal's spirit lives in this totem. Some Aborigines will tell you that they can change into their totem, that is, become a kangaroo, or an emu, or an eagle, and then, when they wish, change back into a man again.

This totem is something like what many white people believe they have, a guardian angel, or spirit. You ask your mother or father what star you or they were

12

born under, and they will tell you, the Lion, or the Goat, or the Fish. These stars are supposed to help us and guide us in our lives. This superstition of ours goes back to the times when we lived like the Aborigines and had beliefs very much the same as they have.

Of course, the Aborigines can tell you about this better than I can. An old friend of mine, Percy Mumbulla, was telling me about his totem. In his language it is called 'mood-jin-garl'. He said, 'Every kurri (Aboriginal) has a mood-jin-garl. It is given to him before he is born. It's his power, his spirit, which looks after him and warns him of danger. My mood-jin-garl is the owl. If there's danger coming, the owl will sing out in the night to me.

'If I don't take any notice, he'll fly down through the camp and hit me with his wing as he passes. If I still don't take notice he'll swoop down and flutter in the ashes

BUGEEN

of the fire. He'll lie there fluttering as though he's hurt. He'll get up and flutter away and try and lead me off.

'I know there's danger then, close up. Someone, a "bugeen" (an evil spirit) is sneaking up on me to kill me. I've got to grab my swag, straight away, and go. My mood-jin-garl will lead me away until I'm out of danger.'

One day I was telling some white people about an Aboriginal's totem. They didn't believe me. An Aboriginal friend of mine, whose white man's name was James McGrath, was close by. I called him over and said, 'Ngudge (brother), tell these white people about your "barn-yun-bee" (totem).'

James told these white people, 'Well, my totem is the black eagle. Suppose you were out in the bush with me and I wanted to change into my totem, I'd walk behind

13

a big gum tree. You wouldn't see me come from behind it. I'd disappear. After a while you'd see a black eagle cruising around above the tree tops.'

So now, when you read in these stories about men who are animals, birds, or fish, you will know that the Aboriginal who is telling the story is speaking about men and their totems. And speaking about totems, did you know that an old Aboriginal gave me a totem? When he gave it to me he said, 'Now you must call me "yela" (father).' And what is the totem I was given? All right, I'll let you into the secret. It is the rainbow. So you see that the Aborigines believe that the spirit lives in everything.

Most of the stories in this book are stories of the Dreamtime, but some of the stories at the end of the book are about the Aborigines living in the country settled by the white man. Although these Aborigines no longer lead a tribal life, they still remain the children of the Dreamtime.

JAMMUTT, THE WATER-SHOOTING FISH

The Legends

The Whale and the Native Bear

In the remote past, all the people that are now in Australia lived in another land beyond the sea. In those far off days they were human creatures, and decided to leave their own country in canoes, and seek fresh hunting grounds which they knew to exist.

The Whale had a very large canoe which he would not lend to any of his fellows, all of whom had small canoes unsafe for use far from land. So all the unlucky ones watched for the chance to seize the Whale's canoe and paddle away in it to the new country. But the mighty owner kept a strict guard over the biggest canoe in the world.

Now the Whale's closest friend was the Starfish — a false friend, for he planned with other people to take the Whale's attention from his canoe, thus giving them a chance to steal it. One day the Starfish said he would free the Whale's head from sea-lice. The Whale was pleased about this. He tied up his canoe and sat down on a rock beside it.

The Starfish gave a sign to the other people, and then began to scrape away the sea-lice from the Whale's head, which he held in his lap. Every now and again the Whale would ask, 'Is my canoe all right?' The Starfish would say, 'Yes, this is your canoe which I am tapping with my hand.' The Starfish would be tapping a piece of bark beside him.

While this was going on the people had piled into the canoe and paddled away. They were nearly out of sight when the Whale raised his head to make sure that everything was all right. Seeing his canoe gone, the Whale became very angry and, after tearing the Starfish almost to pieces, leaped into the sea and swam after the fugitives.

In his fury the Whale spouted water high into the air through a wound in his head which the Starfish made when he was attacked. The cowardly ones among the people in the canoe became terrified on seeing the Whale coming after them. But the Native Bear, who had charge of the paddles, cried, 'Look at my strong arms! I am able to move the canoe fast enough to make good our escape.' And he paddled so strongly that the Whale was soon left far behind.

The voyage lasted for many days and nights. At length land was sighted, and reaching the shore, all the people from the Land Beyond the Sea alighted from their stolen canoe and sat down to rest themselves. But the Brolga or Native Companion, who, as everyone knows, likes dancing and jumping around, leaped into the canoe and danced until the water came gushing into it through a hole made by the bird's feet.

Jumping overboard, the Brolga shoved the canoe out a little way from the shore. The canoe settled down into the ocean and became the small island Gan-man-Gang, near the entrance of Lake Illawarra.

Soon afterwards the Whale arrived. When he saw what had happened, he turned and swam back along the coast where he and his children have remained ever since.

The First Men

The Melbourne Aborigines say that Pund-jel made two men out of clay. This was in the long, long ages past, and these two men first breathed in a country towards the north-west.

Pund-jel made the two men out of clay—like this: with his big knife he cut three large sheets of bark. On one of these sheets of bark he placed some clay and made it soft and easy to use with his knife.

When the clay was soft, he carried some to one of the other pieces of bark, and began to form the clay into a man. He began at the feet, then he made the legs, then he formed the trunk, and then the arms and the head.

He made a man on each of the two pieces of bark. He was pleased with his work and he looked at the men a long time, and he danced around them.

He next took stringybark from a tree, and made hair of it, and put it on their heads—on one, straight hair, and on the other, curled hair.

He gave a name to each man. The man with the straight hair he called Ber-rook-boorn and the man with the curled hair he called Koo-kin-ber-rook.

After again smoothing their bodies with his hands, from the feet upwards to their heads, he lay upon each of them, and blew his breath into their mouths, into their noses, and into their navels.

Breathing very hard, they stirred.

He danced about them a third time. He then made them speak, and caused them to get up, and they rose up, and they were full-grown young men—not like children.

The First Women

Pal-ly-yan, who is known sometimes as a brother of Pund-jel, and sometimes as a son, has control of the waters, great and small. He is the master of rivers, creeks and lagoons, and the sea obeys him.

There is nothing in the deep waters of the rivers that he does not know, and his main pleasure is to paddle in the shallow waters, and to dive to great depths in the deep waters.

One day he was playing in a deep, deep waterhole. He thumped and threshed the water with his hands, in the same way that women beat the skins when the men dance the corroboree. The water became thick; it became very thick; it became as mud; and Pal-ly-yan could no longer see through it as before. But at length he saw something and dividing the thick waters with a bough, so as to get a glimpse of things underneath, he saw what appeared to be hands, such as Pund-jel had given to the men he had created.

Pal-ly-yan took a strong twig, bent it into the form of a hook, and again divided the waters. And there appeared two heads such as Pund-jel had given to the men, then bodies, like those made by Pund-jel, and at last two young women.

Pal-ly-yan named one Kun-ner-warra, and the other, Ku-ur-ook, and he brought them to his brother Pund-jel, to show him.

Pund-jel gave a woman to each man he had created. Pund-jel put spears into the hands of the men. To each man he gave a spear. And Pal-ly-yan put into the hands of each woman a digging-stick.

Pal-ly-yan spoke to the men and women and told them to live together. He ordered that the men should use their spears for killing the kangaroos, and he told the women to use the digging-sticks to dig roots.

Pund-jel and Pal-ly-yan remained with the four men and women for three days. They showed the men how they should spear the kangaroo and the emu, and they told the women where they could find roots.

On the third day, Pund-jel, Pal-ly-yan and the four men and women sat down. A whirlwind came on the third day when they had all sat down.

On the third day, when they had all sat down, a storm, then a great storm came, and the whirlwind and the storm and the great storm carried Pund-jel and Pal-ly-yan upwards, far away. And the four men and women saw them no more.

The Scattering
of Mankind

There was a time when there were many men and women. In some parts of the earth there were very many, and they were wicked. And Pund-jel became angry. Pund-jel became very sulky when he saw that men and women were many and very bad. He caused storms to rise, and fierce winds to blow often. In the flat lands whirlwinds of great force rose, and on the mountains the big trees were shaken with strong winds.

Pund-jel came down to see the men and women. He spoke to no one. He carried with him his big knife. He went into the camps with his knife, and he cut with his knife. He cut this way and that way. And men, women and children he cut into very small pieces.

But the pieces into which he had cut the men, women, and children did not die. Each piece moved as the worm, Tur-ror, moves. Great, great storms and whirlwinds came and carried away the pieces that moved like worms, and the pieces became like flakes of snow. They were carried into the clouds. The clouds carried the pieces hither and thither over all the earth; and Pund-jel caused the pieces to drop in such places as he pleased.

In this way men and women were scattered over the earth. Pund-jel made stars of the good men and good women. The stars are still in the heavens, and the clever old men can tell which among the stars were once good men and good women.

White Tribe and Black Tribe

A long time ago, there were two tribes living on the banks of a large river. One tribe, who were blackfellows, lived on the southern side of the river. The other tribe, who were whitefellows, lived on the northern side.

For many years the two tribes were friendly towards each other, inter-marrying, merry-making, and holding fighting contests. And so it continued until by and by a change of feeling came over the northern tribe.

This white tribe was more powerful, athletic and agile than the black tribe. They made better spears, boomerangs and other arms, and could use them better than the poor southmen.

The northmen became proud and would not have anything to do with the southmen, except in the fighting contests, and in the matter of fighting, the proud whitefellows always came off best.

Things went on in this way for a great number of years, until one day it began to rain. The rain poured down for many months, and the river overflowed its banks and made the blackfellows journey far away from their country towards the south.

The flood was as long in going down as it had been in rising, and it was a long time before the blackfellows could return to their country.

When they did return they could not believe what they saw. In place of the river, which in the old days they had been able to cross, a vast sea rolled to the north of them.

The proud whitefellows had vanished, and were never seen again or heard of by the blackfellows.

Uli-tarra
and his Warriors

The first man came from the East, or the land where the sun rises. His name was Uli-tarra.

In the beginning there was no sea or water, except in a deep hole or well on a mountain. Uli-tarra made this hole or well and he called it Koola-bul-amba, which means a hole or well where the eagles drink.

Uli-tarra led his tribe of Aborigines to fight a tribe who lived in a country beyond the mountains. Before starting out for the fight, they painted themselves with **red** ochre and white ochre.

On the journey Uli-tarra caught and beat two young women. The two young women walked away, and finding two straight sticks growing in the ground, cut one each, and then beat the ground. The ground made a hollow, humming sound.

After this, the two young women parted, one going to the north, the other to the south. Both kept on travelling in the opposite directions, until they met at the other end of the country. There are two rocks in that place now.

The beating with the sticks by the two young women made the ocean and the creeks which run into it.

Those who had started for the fight, having beaten the tribe beyond the mountains, started back rejoicing, throwing their spears and boomerangs ahead of them as they travelled.

One of the boomerangs made a splash in water, and the man who threw it said, 'What, is that my boomerang in water?'

Another boomerang was thrown, and it also splashed up water. The throwers then went to get their boomerangs. They found that the sea covered what was dry land before they had gone on their journey.

They were frightened to find that the sea had cut them off from their country and their hunting grounds. They tried to cross with a long rope. Some people say that they took the entrails of a native bear and blew through them. Those entrails went up into the sky. They curved up into the sky and made a bridge over the sea.

This story says that two clever men made the rope out of the entrails of a native bear. They got the rope across the sea and tied it to a tree. Then another rope was taken across and tied to the tree, only a little higher up, so that the Aborigines could hold on to it while walking across.

As they were walking across, one Aboriginal wanted to eat the rope. This man was called the native cat, and he was told by the Aborigines not to eat or cut the rope.

The warriors led by Uli-tarra then crossed over safely. They saw nothing more of the tribe they had fought and beaten.

The Rainbow-Snake

In the Dreamtime the old man Nagacork made a long and deep waterhole in the Flying-fox River.

And the old man went on a long walkabout and, returning to the billabong, saw the smoke of many campfires rising through the pandanus palms and paperbark trees. He heard the talking and laughter of the many tribes camped among the deep shady trees. And as he came along the river bank he saw the tribesmen swimming and spearing for fish.

He saw the lubras and children wading among the lilies and feeling with their hands and feet in the deep mud for the lily-bulbs and mussels. And the lubras were singing and calling to one another as they pushed the boat-like coolamons over the water to one another to hold the food they were gathering.

And when the tribesmen saw the old man Nagacork they called out to him, 'Come on, old man, there's plenty of fish here, plenty of barramundi.' But the old man Nagacork was quiet and said little to them. And Nagacork went on through the trees along the river bank, and parties of tribesmen and lubras going about from camp to camp passed him as he went.

Nagacork was looking for Jammutt, his water-shooting fish, and he had not seen them in any part of the river. And he turned back again and as the tribesmen saw him coming they called out to him and pointed to various fish in the river. Other tribesmen ran along the bank, pointing and calling, 'Here, old man, are these the fish you are looking for?'

25

'No,' said Nagacork, 'they are not my fish. It does not matter. I'll go to my camp.'

And as Nagacork went slowly along he saw a stream of ants passing and repassing and leading over the ground to a big coolibah tree. The stream of ants went up the bark of the tree and, high up on the trunk, disappeared into a large hole. And Nagacork climbed up the tree and looked down into the hole. And soon, in the darkness, he saw the bones of Jammutt, his lost water-shooting fish. The tribesmen had killed and eaten them and had hidden the bones there.

And the old man climbed down the tree and went and made his camp under a clump of pandanus palms. And he sat with his head on his arms across his knees. He was thinking about his lost fish. And as he sat there he began to sing to himself: 'I wait, wait, wait, wait, wait.'

Suddenly it seemed to him that he was singing up Kurrichalpongo, the black rock-snake. And high in a paperbark tree above him, Dat-dat, the green parrot, began to call out that he could see the great rock-snake coming out of the mountains in the north from a place on the Wilton River.

And then, far in the sky, above the tops of the trees, the old man Nagacork saw the wide curve of a rainbow appearing.

And Kurrichalpongo the rock-snake went under the ground and came and bored a hole in the bank of the billabong and let out a rush of water to drown all the tribes.

As the tribesmen were swimming and wading in the billabong, they saw the water rising. At first the water was up to their thighs, then it was up to their chests. And the water rose and covered the reeds and lilies. It rose and spread over the banks and covered the camps of the many tribes and drowned the tribesmen as it rose.

And there many of the tribesmen changed themselves into birds and flew up and away over the water, screaming harshly as they went. And some, to escape from drowning, changed into Kooroopir the tortoise, and Wooreyong the long-necked tortoise.

And at this place, called Talawung, the black rock-snake laid many eggs and brought out young rainbow-snakes. And some of these eggs were turned into stone and are there to this day.

The young rainbow-snakes started off to travel in different directions. But Kurrichalpongo went on to Yooloo, which is on the Wilton River. And as the black rock-snake went along she looked back and saw that the winding track she was making was turning into a deep wide river with trees and reeds and lilies. Far behind her she saw billabongs gleaming in the sun. And again she looked back and saw all the bush and the mountains springing up behind her. 'What is happening?' said Kurrichalpongo. 'How am I doing this?'

Then, on a plain in the Mainoru country, Kurrichalpongo met and fought with Kandagun the dingo. After fighting off the dingo, the black rock-snake lay down to rest and, on rising, she found she had made the bitter yams that grow there.

Travelling on, Kurrichalpongo made a big swamp. She went on and came to Munaringi, which is where the Roper River flows into the sea. And she travelled on and came to Luralingi, which is at the Hodgson River.

At Luralingi two lubras of the Maranbella tribe had run away from their husbands. They had found two young men who were sons of Nagacork. Now these two young men had found a lot of little rainbow-snakes in a tree and in a cave nearby.

The two men cut down the tree and killed the snakes that were in it, and they went into the cave and killed the young snakes there.

And the two young men took all these snakes along to their father Nagacork to show him what they had killed for food. But when Nagacork saw the snakes he frowned and said, 'You should not have done this. Those are rainbow-snakes you have killed. You must die for doing this.'

And when Kurrichalpongo came to Luralingi she turned into Bolong the rainbow-snake. And as she did so, lightning with many tongues forked out into the sky and thunder came with noise of mountains being split apart with huge rocks crashing down and the sound of their falling ever following and echoing away.

The rain and wind came snapping off and uprooting trees. And the mountains fell down on the tribes and the water came, swirling trees and tribesmen together as it rushed along.

And the tribes who were drowned there were the Wallipooroo, the Mara, the Yookul, the Karkaringi, the Yarnyoola, the Binbinga, the Narnga and the Karawa.

Bolong the rainbow-snake turned back into Kurrichalpongo and went down into the ground.

Kurrichalpongo travelled to Moorinjairee, which is Newcastle Waters. There she met the old man Nagacork and four other rainbow-snakes. And there they held a big meeting and made corroborees.

And at this place called Moorinjairee, where there are hundreds of waterholes, the Dreamtime ended and all the animals there turned into tribesmen. And Kurrichalpongo and the rainbow-snakes went down into the ground.

The Two White Cranes

The old man Nagacork lay down in the shade of a fig-tree and went to sleep and dreamed. When he awoke he had a new song and corroboree in his mind. He called to two of his sons and said, 'Try over this song and corroboree and see if it is any good. I will sing it to you.'

And Nagacork's two sons learned the corroboree from him, and said that it was good. And Nagacork said to his sons, 'Take, then, the forms of two white cranes. I will call both of you "Eai." You must fly to the different countries of the tribesmen and show and teach them this corroboree.'

And the two sons turned into two white cranes and flew away down the sky to do the bidding of their father.

The Water of Life

When Koopoo, the red plain-kangaroo, was travelling from Arnhem Land towards the eastern sea, he met Jabbor, the native cat. Jabbor asked Koopoo to give him half of the secret ceremonies which belonged to Koopoo.

Koopoo said, 'No. These corroborees are all mine.'

Then Jabbor said that he would fight Koopoo for them. But Koopoo called up all the tribesmen. The tribesmen speared Jabbor with a flight of spears. And this is why Jabbor comes to have white spots all over him, for these spots are the holes the spears made.

And as Jabbor lay dying, Deert, the moon, came along and said to him, 'If you will drink this water of mine you will always be able to come back to life.'

But there were many other native cats there who heard Deert say this, and they would not let Jabbor drink.

'Very well then' said Deert the moon. 'Now you must all die, animals, tribesmen, everybody must die for ever. If you had drunk this water, you would all have been able to come back to life. I shall die, but you will see me return. I am Deert the moon.'

28

The Rainbow-Snake
and the Flying-Foxes

A tribesman of the bat totem had made a fire. He sat down beside it. Two men, a red flying-fox man, and a black flying-fox man, saw the smoke of his fire and came up to it. They sat down at the fire. Now the bat tribesman smelled the different sweat of these two men. 'Tjeeng!' he sneezed. 'You two men have a different skin from me.'

The two flying-fox men looked at one another. 'What's the matter? This man has smelled you and me different from himself. Come on, we'll go.'

The two men went back to find their father, the Rainbow-Snake. 'Father,' said the red flying-fox man, 'what is the matter? A man has smelled us as different from himself. He said we have a different skin. Father, we have to go and kill that man.'

Now a big tribe of flying-fox men were camped along the river. The Rainbow-Snake spoke to them, 'Go now, all you red flying-fox men and black flying-fox men.'

The toad-fish man was a friend of the bat tribesman. He came up and sat at his fire. He growled at the bat tribesman. 'Why have you made trouble with the flying-fox men? You are a proper humbug. By and by a big mob of those men will come here.'

'No matter ' the bat tribesman said. 'I am not frightened. I can stand up to them.'

Now the flying-fox men travelled in two parallel lines. They came and sat down near the fire of the two friends. The red flying-fox man spoke: 'We have big trouble here. We must make a corroboree.'

Now the bat tribesman and the toad-fish man had brought up a big company of tribesmen. The flying-fox men called out to them, 'Come on, you fellows want to see us make this corroboree. Then you will know why you have smelled us differently.'

The bat tribesman stood some distance away from the flying-fox men. Then all the flying-fox men threw their spears at him. But their spears all missed the bat tribesman. Now the toad-fish man came and stood with the bat tribesman. Together they dodged the spears. The toad-fish man lay down and rolled about on the ground. He could not get speared.

Those two friends began to cry out to the flying-fox men, 'Hah! Your spears can't catch us!' Clever were those two men.

Now the Rainbow-Snake came up. He sat down watching the big flights of spears going. More, more, more and more the flights of spears came. The bat tribesman dodged this way, that way; like this, like that. Then a spear caught him through the hips. The toad-fish man pulled out the spear. He lifted his friend onto his shoulders and carried him away to a shade of branches.

Then all the flying-fox men asked their father, the Rainbow-Snake, 'What are we going to do, father?' All the flying-fox men were talking together: 'We will go back. We will go back along the mangroves.'

The Rainbow-Snake was looking for trees that had flowers. He could find nothing, nothing, nothing. 'I will have to take you, all my sons, back to the water,' the

Rainbow-Snake said.

At the river the Rainbow-Snake cut and made a large and long hollow bamboo. He filled up this bamboo with flying-fox men. He blocked the end of the bamboo and put it down into the water. He filled up another bamboo with flying-fox men and put that down into the water. Then the Rainbow-Snake took his fishing net and filled this with flying-fox men and put it down into the water. Under the water he kept the flying-fox men all day.

The Rainbow-Snake stood right up out of the water on his nails near his tail. Now all the trees sprang up, and the trees were in flower. The Rainbow-Snake called out the names of the trees. The gum tree with red flowers. The gum tree with white flowers. The Rainbow-Snake stood up out of the water and looked about him and the paperbark trees sprang up. They flowered with white flowers, and the Rainbow-Snake gave them their name.

The Rainbow-Snake took the dilly-bag hanging from his neck. He held it and let the flying-foxes stream out of it and up into the trees. The flying-foxes called out, 'What food shall we find?'

The Rainbow-Snake said, 'Those red flowers will give you food.'

The Rainbow-Snake let another lot of flying-foxes stream into the white flowering trees. He let go another lot into the paperbark trees. 'There is your food in the flowering trees,' he called.

And again the Rainbow-Snake stood up out of the water and looked around. The trees began to spring up everywhere. 'Oh, the bloodwood tree is good for food,' he cried. 'Oh, the ironwood tree is good for food. When these trees lose their flowers, put your tongues, flying-foxes, along the leaves of the ironwood trees, there you will find your food.'

Out of the dilly-bag, the bamboos and the fishing net the Rainbow-Snake let the flying-foxes stream. And the trees in flower were bent down with the flying-foxes hanging to them.

Always now the Rainbow-Snake puts the bamboo to his mouth and blows out the spirits of the flying-foxes. He makes a spray of water and the rainbow curves over his head. And the bands in the rainbow are the spirits of the flying-foxes blown out of the bamboo of the Rainbow-Snake.

The Spirit-Children

I

In the place called Nimaluk where spring-water is bubbling up, the Rainbow-Snake made a wide, clear space. In this place, the Rainbow-Snake set lines of stones. He said, 'These stones I put out in a dry place. These stones contain the spirits of my men-children. All my girl-children I will keep with me in the water. I put the name Nimaluk to this spring-water. And to this creek I put its name. We cannot lose this country. We stop here. We watch this place called Nimaluk.'

In another place the Rainbow-Snake made a big clear space again. He set stones all round this place. And the Rainbow-Snake said, 'In these stones are the spirits of my fish-children, the mullet.' And in other places the Rainbow-Snake set stones for his spirit-children: the dingo, the tortoise and the goose.

An old man camped near the place Nimaluk. He found plenty of food there, fish, tortoise, goanna and yam. In a light from the water, the Rainbow-Snake sent a spirit-child to that old man's wife. When the child was born, it was a girl. Everyone said. 'Oh, what a pretty girl.' 'Oh, what good hair this girl has.' 'This is a good baby.'

The old man said, 'The Rainbow-Snake has sent his child from the water.'

The spirit-child may be in a fish, goanna, tortoise, or a goose, or anything that is speared for food. When this food is taken back to the camp, the spirit-child finds its mother there.

For the same reason a child called Moitta was born with a crooked arm, because his brother had been out hunting and had speared a goose with a spirit-child inside it. He broke the goose's wing and took it back to the camp. And the spirit-child inside the goose went to his mother and was born as Moitta with the crooked arm.

The Spirit-Children

II

One day my father found a big billabong. He climbed a tree to look out over the billabong. 'Oh,' he cried, 'there's plenty of geese here.' The geese did not fly away. They went on feeding in the grass and in the billabong. As my father was catching the geese, a rainbow came up in the sky. The rainbow came right over his head. My father took plenty of geese back to the camp.

When my father came back to the camp my mother asked him: 'What is the matter? Are you sick?'

'Oh,' said my father, 'I found a big water and caught plenty of geese. Then something in the sky came right over my head.'

33

Now the Rainbow-Snake had blown out all those geese from along his tongue. He had made that rainbow go right over my father's head. After that, my mother knew that she was going to have a baby.

And the lightning, which belongs to the Rainbow-Snake, makes spirit-children. He comes up. He kills trees. He breaks them up. Everybody asks, 'What's the matter?' 'Something is here.' Everybody gets frightened. By and by, one woman has a baby. The Rainbow-Snake makes fish this way, he makes geese, anything.

One day my father stood on a hill and looked out a long way over the salt water. He saw a long line of seaweed. The tide was bringing it in. As my father stood on the hill he heard the sound of the bamboo drone-pipe of the Rainbow-Snake in the salt water. 'Boom, boom, shsh, shsh.' The Rainbow-Snake was blowing the spirit-children out of his bamboo: one line of fish, one line of fish, one line of seaweed.

All right, this one finish. A big wind blew, blew all day. My brother came up out of the salt water to my mother.

No more the Rainbow-Snake blows his bamboo drone-pipe from the dry country, always from water. Sometimes he sends a pretty baby. When a rainbow is close up to the camp and he sends a baby, it comes from water. The rain falls straight down. The rainbow comes. The Rainbow-Snake makes those children, the spirit-children.

The Old Man
and the Rainbow-Snake

Two boys had been out gathering the roots called tjarmo for poisoning fish. They dug the roots up, put them inside two bundles of paperbark, and took them back to the camp. There they hung the two bundles up in a tree. One old man talked to those two boys, 'You have been out to get tjarmo?'

'Yes, old man,' said the two boys. 'We have got two paperbark bundles.'

'Well,' said the old man, 'you must not take any girl or little boy with you when you go after those fish. If you do, by and by you find no more fish.'

At daylight those two boys got a flat stone and a round stone. They sat down and crushed up those roots, tjarmo, between the stones. They put the crushed roots back in the paperbark and took them away to a billabong. The boys waded into the billabong and threw in the poison roots. They waded and swam about, stirring the water up.

Those two boys came out of the billabong and sat down and watched for the fish. By and by fish began to come up. The poison roots had made those fish stupid. They lay on their sides trying to swim and floated upside down. There were black bream, rifle-fish, barramundi and catfish. The two boys speared them, speared them, and threw them out on to the banks.

The two boys went down into the billabong and stirred up the water again. The water was up to their waists. The two boys speared and speared plenty of fish. The water crept up to their chests. Those two boys did not look, they went on spearing fish. The water was creeping up and up.

'Oh,' cried the boys, 'we have plenty of fish.'

'That old man told us.'

'Yes, we have plenty for that old man, plenty for our uncle, our granny.'

Still the water crept up and up.

The Rainbow-Snake had made that water rise in the billabong. He sent a big barramundi for those boys to spear. The boys found the water was up to their chins. 'Oh, something is wrong,' they cried. 'We must go.'

It was too late. The Rainbow-Snake grabbed those two boys. He took them under the water, under the ground. He took them a long way, along a dry country, under the ground.

That old man had sat down in the camp waiting for those two boys. He waited, waited. No more those boys came back. That old man had heard a noise like thunder when the Rainbow-Snake took those two boys.

The old man went to the billabong. He came up and saw the billabong brimming with water. The water was all churned up. It was turning over and over. The old man listened. 'Ah,' he said, 'the Rainbow-Snake has taken those two boys.'

The old man listened. 'Ah,' he said, 'this way that Rainbow-Snake has gone.'

He ran. He stopped and pounded on the ground with his foot. He broke through the ground. He felt with his foot. The hollow under the ground was empty.

The old man ran on again. He put his ear to the ground and listened. He broke through the ground with his foot. He felt in the hollow with his arm. Nothing! the hollow was empty. The old man ran on. He stopped and listened. He broke through the ground. He felt in the big hollow. 'Ah,' he said, 'I feel that Rainbow-Snake.'

The old man dug out mud. He sang the Rainbow-Snake. He felt along that big hollow. He felt one boy. He pulled that boy out. The Rainbow-Snake did not go away. The old man sang the Rainbow-Snake. The old man felt about. He pulled out the other boy. He took those boys and washed them along water. The Rainbow-Snake had slimed those boys all over.

The old man put those boys out in the sun. He sang those two boys to make them come alive again. He sang them, sang them. By and by ants came up and bit those boys all over. Those two boys flinched when the ants bit them, they moved. The old man watched the boys, he sang them.

By and by those two boys opened their eyes, they sat up, they looked around. That old man talked, 'Well, my boys, next time you want to poison fish, you poison ten fish, then bring them quickly up along the camp.'

'Yes, Yela, old man.' Those two boys talked.

That old man took those boys back to the camp. Their mother and their grandmother cried when they saw them. They cried to that old man, 'Ah, you are a properly clever old man. You have brought back our two boys.'

The Spirit Malingee

Malingee is the spirit who travels at night. He is on a long walkabout and is going home. As he walks along he knocks his knees together. He looks for tucker as he goes. He finds and kills rock-wallabies, bandicoots and eagle-hawks. In the song of Malingee, that is sung in the Djauan tribe, he is going to Munjoowooroo, to Kandawool, to Mirri-mirri-wongo, and to Man-lut-boora. And he is going to his home at Baramun-junga, which is where the river flows through Mainoru station.

And if Malingee meets any tribesmen, he kills them with his stone axe. He has sharp stone knives on his elbows, and his eyes are burning in his devil's face.

37

The Morning Star

On Buralku, the Island of the Spirits of the Dead, two spirits made the morning star. From the skin of the banyan tree they made the string and twisted the white downy feathers of birds in it. The tuft of white feathers on the end of the string they made from the feathers of the whistle-duck, the jabiru, the brolga, the spoonbill, and the ibis.

When the two spirits want to speak with spirits in other countries, they throw the tuft of white feathers, which is the morning star, into the sky. And, when it is daylight, they pull the morning star, on the end of his string, down again to Buralku, the Island of the Spirits of the Dead.

The morning star on the end of his string lies coiled up in the dilly-bag of one old-man spirit. This dilly-bag is the mother of the morning star. The tuft of white feathers, the morning star, is the child looking out of the dilly-bag.

On the island of Buralku two sisters say to those two spirits, 'Are you going to send out the morning star?'

'Not yet,' the old-man spirit says. 'You must dance first.' The old man hits his song-sticks together and sings. Then the two sisters dance and sing, and cut their heads with yam-sticks because they are sorry to see the child, the morning star, going away from them.

The old man dances, holding the dilly-bag with the morning star in it. He looks around as he dances and sees a pandanus tree. He throws the morning star out of the dilly-bag and the star climbs up the pandanus and goes into the dark sky.

'I send this morning star,' sings the old man, 'to a little island in the salt water.' The morning star goes into the sky, and then it is daylight. Then the old man pulls the star down and puts him back in the dilly-bag.

Day and night this spirit dances and the sisters cut themselves on their heads with yam-sticks because they are sorry to send the morning star away.

In the night time the old man talks, 'We must send the morning star a long way and make daylight in another country.' The spirits hit the song-sticks and the two sisters dance and cut themselves with the yam-sticks. The old man throws the morning star and he goes away up into the sky.

The old man talks to the spirit Yangoor on the little island. 'It is daylight now. Catch hold of the string and pull down the morning star.' The string of the morning star is dangling down out of a pandanus tree. Yangoor pulls the morning star down and puts him in his dilly-bag.

Yangoor talks back to the old man, 'I keep this morning star. I have a big ceremony now.'

Now on this island a little boy ran and caught hold of the dilly-bag and the morning star. He climbed up the pandanus tree because he wanted to throw the morning star too. Yangoor caught the boy by the waist and pulled him back. 'You

cannot send the star,' said Yangoor. 'You are only a little boy. I must send him. I am an old man.'

In a country near Buckingham Bay, the morning star lands in a pandanus. A woman in that country pulls the star down on his feathered string. This woman says, 'Oh, this star belongs to me now. Oh, this is my child, my morning star.'

It is night time. In that country are many spirits of the dead. The spirits make a big song to call on the morning star. They sing, 'Climb up, morning star, climb up the white milkwood tree.'

One old man takes the star from the woman. He paints the tuft of feathers with red ochre. 'Are you going to send my star a long way?' asks the woman.

'No,' says the old man. 'I will make the string a little bit short.' He throws the star and he climbs up the milkwood tree and goes into the sky.

The red morning star stops at Elcho Island. There a woman is living alone. She has no husband or children. She sees the red star and pulls it down out of a pandanus tree. 'Is this my morning star which you have sent?' she asks.

'Yes,' calls back the old man. 'You can have the red morning star. We have the white one. That is your star and your ceremony. You can throw the red morning star.'

The old man makes another morning star. He throws the star a long way. The star does not come back because all the string has gone out of the dilly-bag. In a country near the Clyde River, the star lands in a banyan tree. There a spirit and his sister see it. 'Oh, brother, the morning star is here,' his sister calls. 'This star belongs to you and me.'

At midnight this brother makes a big song. His sister dances and cries and cuts her head. She does not want to lose that morning star. Her brother throws the star and he goes out into the dark sky. He lands in a milkwood tree near Cape Stewart. There it is daylight and a spirit pulls down the star and puts him in his dilly-bag.

This is the story of the ceremony of the morning star.

The Water-Lubra

A man called Nalul came out of the desert country. He came to a deep, green billabong. Paperbark trees, fig trees, and pandanus palms crowded its banks. Red lotus lilies were open among their broad leaves floating on the water.

As the man walked through the deep shade of the trees, he heard voices, girls' voices, talking and laughing. He did not know the language. It was like the sound of water running over stones, or splashing into a pool.

Like the shadow of an eagle passing, he moved over the leaves. He moved through sunlight and shadow. He sneaked up to where the voices came from. Through the tall reeds and bulrushes he saw the glitter of stirred water. The splashings and laughter were close up. He parted the reeds. He made them rustle. The splashings and laughter stopped. He looked down on the water. It was stirred up. He thought he saw something like long hair swirling down into the billabong.

The man camped in that place. In the morning he went out to spear fish. Near the billabong he stopped to drink at a spring bubbling out of the ground. He heard a girl's voice singing. It was like the sound of the spring water.

Nalul made no sound. He moved over the leaves. Through the trees he could see a part of the billabong with a sandy shore. The singing was coming from there. He sneaked up, sneaked up. He was close up to that singing. There, just beyond the young paperbark tree he stood behind, was a girl. She was lying on the sand, in the sunlight, near the edge of the water. Her long wet hair streamed down over her shoulders. She was resting on one elbow. She shook back her hair as she sang.

Nalul made one spring from behind the paperbark tree. He caught that girl. He caught her by her long hair. The girl fought him. She bit him on the arm, the

41

shoulder. Nalul wound her hair round his forearm and gave it to her to bite. He scooped sand and threw it in her eyes.

At last the girl was tired. He carried her away. He got fig tree cord and tied her wrists and ankles. He tied her to a paperbark tree.

He went away. He brought back honey in a paperbark coolamon. He put the honey near the girl. He untied her a little. He went away. He sat down and watched her through the leaves.

The girl did not understand that food. After a while she reached out a hand. She touched the honey with her finger. She tasted the honey. She kept on tasting it.

The man Nalul came back. The girl could not understand, nor speak his language. Nalul wiped sweat from his body. He wiped his sweat across her mouth, her eyes, her ears.

He got bark. He heated the bark in fire. He pressed the bark against the girl's ears to get the sound of the water out of them. The girl spoke his language. Now she could properly see and hear him. Nalul told her, 'I call you Nyal Warrai-Warrai.' This means the girl from the water.

The girl followed Nalul. They travelled. They did not camp near any waterhole. Nalul got bandicoot, possum, goanna, and honey. He taught the girl to eat his food.

They travelled into the desert country. Nalul did not take the girl to his tribe. They camped alone near water soaks, never near rivers or waterholes. Wallaby, honey-ants, wild figs and little yams those two found for their food. Three moons they stayed in the desert.

The girl was sorry for her country. They went back to the country called Mùngun. It has no white man's name. They camped near a big spring. They found plenty of food there. Nalul said to the girl, 'Take the coolamon and get water. I will go and get firewood.'

The girl went down to the spring. The spring went down under the ground to the big billabong where Nalul first saw the girl.

As the girl filled the coolamon at the spring, she saw all the girls, the Nyal Warrai-Warrai, rising from the water. 'Oh, sister, sister!' they cried out. 'Come quickly, quickly. By and by that man will come back.'

Nalul's girl wanted to go back to him but her sisters cried out to her. They dived down into the spring. Then the girl belonging to Nalul dived in after them.

The man Nalul came back with the firewood. He waited in the camp. He got up. He ran to the spring. Nothing. The girl was gone. There, at the edge of the spring, was the coolamon the girl had thrown away.

The man dived into the spring. He swam down and down. Then the water was clouded, dark. He could see nothing. He swam back.

Nalul cried for that girl. He cut and cut his head with a sharp stone. He went to the billabong with the red lilies. He sat on the sand by the water and sang Tjarada songs to call that girl up out of the water. No more that girl came back. She had gone to her father, the Rainbow-Snake.

The Place of Devils

In the Dreamtime an old devil woman called Marm sat down in the shade on the top of some rocks at a place called Munjajawa, which the white man calls Cave Creek.

And this old devil woman had no eyes. And it was in the rain-time, and the old woman had a big mob of girls gathering and bringing her the plums called woial.

The old woman, with a huge stone, was crushing up the plums and seeds on the rocks. She was making a big damper, called abbait, out of them. And she called to the girls, 'Bring more! And more yet!' And as fast as the girls brought the old woman the plums, she went on crushing and grinding them on the stone.

The old woman went on crushing the plums until she had ground a deep round hole in the stone. And she made many heaps of this damper and gave it to the girls to eat. And there was so much damper that the girls could not finish it up, but, after eating of it, they were all turned into the devils called Marm.

And Jaleetjee is the name of the rock with the big hole ground in it, and all about it are the heaps of damper which are now turned into stone.

Suppose you were to camp in this place of devils, you would hear someone sing out. You would look up among the rocks or in the grass. You would go over to where the voice came from. There would be no one there. Then, from another place, you would hear someone cutting a tree for 'sugar-bag'. You would go over and there would be no one.

These devils sing out from one place. You go over, and they sing out from another distant place. Suppose you go alone and camp in that place. You see a fire through the trees. You hear a baby crying. You hear the sound of talk-talk. You go over, and there is nothing there. Suppose you stay in that place. You go mad. You never find those devils Marm.

And all that country around is called Woomboo, the country of the devils.

44

Najara the Spirit

One day a tribesman called Najara told his tribe that he was going out to spear an emu. He started out over the plain until he came to a plum tree. But instead of climbing up into the tree and sitting hidden there until the emu came along to find any fallen plums, Najara sat on the ground with his back against the tree.

After he had been sitting there for some time, he saw a big dingo coming along with his nose to the ground as he smelled out the way a goanna had gone. Najara fitted his spear into his throwing-stick, drew back his arm, and speared the dingo.

The dingo rolled over, biting at the spear, and cried out, 'Yakai! Yakai!' And soon many dingoes came running up and began to attack Najara, biting and ripping him. Najara fought them with his stone tomahawk, but the dingoes were too many, they were leaping and streaming over him. And the dingoes ripped up Najara and killed him.

And the moon-man, whose name was Deert, came along and found Najara and buried him. And Najara waited for three days under the ground and then came out.

And Deert, the moon, asked Najara to tell him this cleverness. But Najara said, 'No more. You are Deert. You don't need my cleverness. I am going to find a quiet country now. I am going into the desert.'

Now a boy belonging to the tribe had gone walking over the plains of the long grass. He heard someone whistling to him. And the boy called out, 'Who are you?' And a voice called back, 'I am Najara.'

The boy went over to the place where the voice came from and found Najara sitting in the grass. And the two of them camped together and went away for a long walkabout which lasted many months.

And one day they came back into the Djauan country. Some tribesmen, among whom was the boy's father, saw Najara and the boy standing in the grass on some high, rocky ground.

The tribesmen started to sneak up on these two, until the boy saw them coming and called out to Najara. But Najara did not seem to be alarmed and whistled back to the boy. But, when the tribesmen came up, Najara was gone.

And the tribesmen chased the boy for a long time until they caught him and tied him up. And the boy was like a wild animal and the tribesmen kept him tied up until he would eat and was quietened and had remembered his own language and knew his father again.

And the spirit of Najara still whistles out of the grass and scrub to tribesmen and leads them away into the desert country until they have forgotten their language and their tribe.

The Crocodile-Man

An old man named Karabulla found this country the first time. He sat down along the waterholes all the time. He is still here. He has plenty of lily-tucker. When the floodwater comes that old man goes out along the plain. When the floodwater goes away that old man comes back. He is an old man. He has white whiskers. He is crocodile too. You can hear him when you come for water. He is in the waterhole. He calls out, 'Oi! Oi! Brrpm!' You think he's a crocodile. He's an old man.

I've seen that old man. He has his own road. He has white whiskers, long feller moustache. We leave that old man alone. If we touch him, that water will go away.

One day my son speared that old man in the leg. Well, afterwards, my son became silly in the head. I heard that old man in the waterhole. I asked the old man Mardinga, 'Is that old man in the waterhole a crocodile?'

Mardinga said, 'No more. He is an old man. He's a funny old man. He jumps up in the waterhole. He calls out, "Hoi!" '

One time we came to a waterhole. I said to Mardinga, 'Hey, what's that? Is that a crocodile? Shall I spear him?'

Old man Mardinga said, 'No more, Leave him. He is all right. Poor beggar, he's a funny old man.'

One time I was out on a plain after goose eggs. I saw all these geese fly up. I thought, 'Those geese are frightened. Might be a dingo or something's there.' All those geese flew away. I picked up the goose eggs and put them in my dilly-bag. I saw one road, one path through the grass. I followed and followed that path. Soon, I saw that old man. That old man looked back. I saw his white whiskers. It was in the rain-time. A path went through the grass. No track. There was water there. That old man laughed at me, 'Hoo-hoo-hoo.' He threw out his white whiskers as he went along. He was in the waterhole. His mouth was full of lily-bulbs. He laughed, spat out lily-bulbs into his hands, chucked them away over the water, and dived under.

An old man, Tjimarr, was diving after tortoises. He did not come up. Everyone dived into the waterhole and swam down. They could not find that old man. The crocodile old man had shut up Tjimarr somewhere down in the water.

Tjimarr's wife sat down and cried all day along that water. The crocodile old man was sorry for her. He said to Tjimarr, 'You can go. You go this way. Look, see that hole where you came in?'

Tjimarr came up out of the waterhole, but he was full of water. My son was there. He caught hold of Tjimarr. He held him upside down and emptied the water out of him.

That crocodile old man is still here. He found this country the first time.

Perentie and Goanna

Tjonba is my name. It means perentie, the big desert goanna. An old man took me walkabout. We were out hunting. The old man called out to me, 'Oh, boy, come over here.' The old man showed me a big flat stone. In that stone were the tracks of Tjonba the perentie and alongside were the tracks of Looartjarra the little goanna.

Two old men, perentie and goanna, came out of a big cave. These two old men started travelling away. They camped and the goanna went to sleep. Old perentie talked: 'Old man, wake up! I will put a paint on you that will make all the girls want to see you.'

Old goanna began to yabber: 'All right, all right. But don't you spoil me.'

Old goanna crouched down on the ground. Old perentie painted him with red ochre, white clay, and charcoal. When old goanna got up he dropped something. Old perentie said, 'Old man, you dropped something there.' It was a white stone.

Those two fellows had a good look at that stone. 'Oh,' said the old goanna, 'it's no good.'

Old perentie said, 'Well, we might make a fire with that stone.' The stone was a white opal with fire in it. Old perentie picked up the stone and carried it about with him.

The two old men travelled on. After a while old goanna called out, 'Old man! Oh my leg, my back, my foot! I'm tired. Let's make a fire. That cave is a long way behind now.'

Old goanna got some kangaroo droppings. He rubbed them into powder. He gathered some sticks and bushes. He called out to old perentie, 'Hey, old man, lend me that stone. We'll make a fire.' He sat down, struck the stone on another stone and made fire. Those two old fellows went to sleep.

The fire began to blow green, and blue, and red. By and by, the two old fellows woke up and saw that fire. Old goanna says, 'Hey what's the matter with this fire?'

Old perentie says, 'That's mine, don't take any notice of it.' Where those two old

47

men camped there is a big opal reef with black, red, white, and green stones. No white man knows that place. We never tell.

Those two old men got up in the morning-time. They covered over the fire. They started travelling, old goanna in the lead, old perentie behind. Old goanna looked back. 'Old man,' he said, 'what's the matter? Are you tired?'

Old perentie said, 'Oo-er, yes. I must sit down.'

Goanna walked about and brought back a leaf from a bush. 'Here, old man. Eat that.' He threw the leaf to perentie. Old perentie ate one side of the leaf, old goanna ate the other side.

The two old men came to a waterhole. After they drank, old goanna turned his shoulder round and looked at himself in the water. He turned right round and looked at his head, his back and his tail. Then he stood right up on his tail and leaned back and looked at himself. He called out to perentie, 'Old man, you missed me in one place.'

Perentie painted and painted goanna again. 'Look at yourself now,' he said.

Old goanna looked at himself in the water again. 'Ah, that's the one, my old mate. I'll never forget you.' 'What about you?' goanna asked perentie.

'Yes, yes, you paint me,' perentie said. Old goanna got a stick. It was too big. He chewed one end and made a brush. Perentie lay down. He went to sleep and goanna painted him with the big brush. 'Wake up, old man. Have a look at yourself along that water,' goanna said.

Old perentie looked at himself in the water. He began to yabber, 'You have put this paint on me too big.'

'No, no,' said goanna, 'girls like that kind of painting.'

Old perentie made a fire, a big smoke. He put leaves on, and smothered the fire. Then the two old men lay down on the leaves to dry the paint on them. Old goanna got a bone and pushed it through his nose to make himself look flash. Old perentie did the same. Then the two old men travelled on.

A tribe of perenties and goannas were looking out from their camp. They saw the two old men. 'Hey, who are these fellows?' they said. 'We don't know them. They must be big travelling men.'

When old perentie saw the camp he forgot that he was tired. Old goanna forgot about his bad back, his leg, and his foot. Old goanna called out to old perentie, 'Hey, old man, there are plenty of girls looking at you.'

The old man perentie in the camp called out to the two old men to come up. Goanna and perentie sat down in the camp. Goanna kept poking perentie in the ribs with his elbow. 'Hey, old man, the girls are looking at you,' he would whisper.

Old goanna pushed old perentie in the ribs, 'Hey, old man, we have to marry tonight,' he said.

Old perentie said, 'Um, um. You going to marry tonight?'

'Oh, yes,' said goanna, 'I have to get married too.'

The old man of the camp gave perentie and goanna a girl each. Old perentie and old goanna made a corroboree. They were dancing in that camp. They danced on a stone tableland at Abminga Creek. Old goanna and old perentie chucked all those opal stones about. They made that reef of the opal places on both sides of the creek.

The Fish-People

In olden times there were some people who had the form of different kinds of fish, but they always roamed about and hunted on the dry land the same as other folk. One day they were camped beside the Barwan River, under a shady tree which grew at the top of a steep bank, at the foot of which was a large, deep waterhole. A heavy thunderstorm came suddenly, and almost put out their fire. After the rain, a strong, piercing wind arose, and everybody became very cold.

An old man, Thuggai, the yellow-belly, told his children to try and rekindle the fire. As they could not do so, he asked Biernuga, the bony-fish, to have a try. Then he asked Kumbal, the bream, and some others, but they all failed, because the wood was very wet on account of the recent heavy shower.

There was among the people a Ngulamanbu, a little fish about four or five inches long, and he said to the yellow-belly, Thuggai, 'Ask my father, Guddhu, the cod-fish, to light the fire for us. He is a clever man and I am sure he can light it.' Thuggai asked the cod-fish, and Guddhu then put some pieces of bark on the fire which was almost out and began to blow the few remaining live coals hard with his breath. The fire began to show signs of coming alight again.

All the people at once crowded close to Guddhu on the windward side, keeping their backs towards the cold wind and their faces in the direction of the fire, in the hope of soon being able to warm themselves.

When Guddhu saw this, he asked the people to get further back and give him more room. They all went round to the leeward side, which allowed the wind to play freely on the smouldering embers; which caused the bark and wood gradually to ignite. Guddhu added plenty of fuel, because he wished to make a good fire which would warm everybody.

On the leeward side there was a very narrow space between the fire and the top of the steep bank which was only of enough width to give standing room for the people. At that moment there came a sudden, strong gust of wind which fanned the fire into a large sheet of flame and caused all the people, as well as Guddhu himself, to step backwards to escape being scorched. They all fell headlong down the bank into the water.

The strength of the gale grew and swept the fire also down the bank and into the river. The people who were swimming about gathered around the fire, which continued to burn under the water, and they have remained there ever since. This is why it is always warmer under the water on a bleak, chilly day than it is in the cold air on the surface.

Lake Boolaboolka

Lake Boolaboolka, in the country of Livingstone, New South Wales, was made in the following manner. A blackfellow stood on some rising ground, near where the lake is now, and tried to throw his boomerang, but it fell to the ground at a little distance. He then lit a fire, at which he warmed the boomerang to make it lithe. He worked it in his hands, putting the proper bend upon it, and threw it again.

This time the boomerang went and tore up the ground, and formed Lake Boolaboolka, and came whizzing back towards its owner. While it was gyrating in the air near him, he blew strongly upon it with his breath, and it went to one side of the lake, and started off along the ground in a winding direction, and dug a watercourse. Then the boomerang came back to the thrower as before, and he blew upon it again, and it went and dug out another watercourse.

Every time the weapon returned to its owner, he gave it fresh vigour with his breath. These actions of the boomerang were repeated until all the watercourses and gullies which now flow into Lake Boolaboolka were made. Then a thunderstorm arose, with much rain, which flowed along the watercourses made for it, and filled the lake.

Some days afterward, the Lake-maker was sitting under a shady tree on its banks, when he saw a number of strange blackfellows coming up to it to make their camp.

The Lake-maker took up his boomerang and threw it with all his might in their direction. The boomerang spun round and round among them, striking each one upon the chin, cutting a triangular piece out of their beards. When this happened, every man became a musk duck, and swam out into the water. This is the reason for the fork in the beard-like pouch of the musk ducks which now live on the lake.

51

The Giant Tree

Long ago, an eagle-hawk, Mullion, had his nest in a high tree which grew on the Barmon River. The eagle-hawk used to go out and catch a blackfellow and carry him away to his nest to feed the eaglets and their mother. This went on for a long time and the Aborigines were unable to help themselves because the tree was of giant girth and reached almost to the sky.

It was made of several different trees all joined into one. There was first a gum-tree, a box-tree next, then a coolibah, then a belar and lastly a pine-tree. This made a height of five trees, all the trees being of giant size.

In the top of the pine-tree was the large nest of the eagle-hawk. If a blackfellow went hunting alone, Mullion would swoop down on him and carry him away in his talons to his nest.

Bones were thrown out and scattered around for some distance about the base of the tree.

Two of the headmen of the blackfellows, Murriwunda and Koomba, went to the foot of the tree and had a talk about the best thing to be done to stop Mullion in his killings. They decided to climb up the tree, carrying a piece of burning stick with them, and set the nest on fire.

Koomba made the first attempt. He climbed up a long way until he was unable to go any further, so he came down again and fell on the ground, tired out. After he felt better, he said to Murriwunda, 'I went far, far up the tree, but could not even see the top from where I was. You are lighter than I am, and may be able to reach the nest.'

Murriwunda took some burning bark, fastened it on the top of his head, and started away up the tree, going round and round the trunk in spiral fashion as he went. He got to the top of the gum-tree, and went on to the box-tree, next the coolibah, then the belar, until at last he reached the pine-tree.

This climbing took up most of the afternoon, and Koomba saw small pieces of bark from the several kinds of trees falling to the ground, by which he knew that his friend was going right up to the nest.

When Murriwunda reached the top of the pine-tree, he took the firebrand, which he carried in his forehead-band, and secretly pushed it in the underside of the eagle-hawk's nest. He told the fire not to burn the nest until he got down again to the ground.

The work of climbing down the tree was very tiresome, but was done in much less time than the climbing up.

Murriwunda was so tired that he lay down on the ground to rest. After a while he felt better, and he and Koomba started away towards their own camp.

When they had got away some distance, they caught a goanna, which they cooked and ate, and sat awhile to rest themselves beside a small waterhole.

Murriwunda then said, 'I could not reach Mullion's nest. I don't know what we can do about him.' Then he gave the usual laugh which blackfellows always do when they say anything which is the opposite of the truth. Shortly he added, 'You watch the

sky in the direction of the tree.'

Koomba looked in the direction of the tree. It was evening and he could see a bright blaze in the distance like a large star, which kept getting bigger every minute. Both of them were very glad, and began to sing some of their tribal songs and beat their boomerangs together.

Murriwunda had told the fire not to burn until he had time to get out of danger. The fire then began to smoulder and the eaglets in the nest began to feel the heat under them. They began to move about under their mother's wings. They said they would feel cooler if they came out and sat on the edge of the nest.

When they got out, they began playing, and they pushed against one of their father's spears, which was sticking into the side of the nest. Their father was sitting on a branch close by, and seeing his spear bent over, went and caught hold of it, and feeling angry with his children for moving it, he said, 'I'll stick the spear so firmly in the nest that you can't move it.'

He caught hold of the spear, and gave it a strong shove downwards. The moment he did this the fire which was smouldering underneath burst through the opening made by the spear, in a great tongue of flame, and burnt them all to death.

The fire burned downwards, eating the branches and the trunk of the tree all the way to the ground, and went on along the roots in all directions.

Some of the big roots, which were only a few feet beneath the grass, were completely burned, leaving a hollow all along their length, into which the top soil fell, leaving winding hollows in the ground like small watercourses. Some of these hollows can be traced for several miles from the place where the great tree stood.

Why the Owl has Large Eyes

Away back in the old times, Weemullee, the owl, and Willanjee, the cyclone, were two young men who were great friends. Although they hunted and had their meals together, and slept in the same camp, and chatted to each other, Willanjee was invisible to his companion. Weemullee, however, was always trying to see Willanjee and kept staring in his direction, which caused his eyes to gradually grow larger and rounder.

When they started out hunting together, Willanjee's weapons were carried along just as any blackfellow would carry them, but he could not be seen. When the two hunters were stalking kangaroos, Weemullee would see Willanjee's spear poised in the womerah, and thrown at the kangaroo. He would hear Willanjee's voice calling out that he had speared the kangaroo. When the two men rushed up to kill the animal, Willanjee's club was being used in an unseen hand. All this puzzled Weemullee and he was forever straining his eyes in vain to see his friend.

One day these two mates were out hunting as usual, and had caught some goannas and black ducks. Towards evening Weemullee climbed a tree and caught a fat young opossum in one of the hollow spouts. Willanjee called out, 'Throw it down to me and we will go home and cook our supper.' Weemullee then came down from the tree and the two mates started for the camp, carrying with them their day's catch of game.

The opossum was carried along by the unseen Willanjee, and when the camp was reached he made a fire and cooked the different animals in the usual native fashion. The hunters had a great feast, and when it was over Willanjee rolled himself up in his rug and lay down by the camp fire. It was then that Weemullee decided that he would have a close look at his friend while he was sound asleep with a full stomach.

By and by, when all was quiet, with his eyes opened to their widest, he carefully unfolded and lifted up one corner of Willanjee's skin rug. The moment the rug was raised, out burst the wind and scattered everything in the camp in all directions. Weemullee was swept into a hollow tree and on up inside, coming out again at a top spout. He was then blown away across a plain, all the time staring and straining his eyes in the hope of seeing his queer companion.

At last he caught a firm hold of a small but tough acacia tree and managed to cling to it till Willangee the whirlwind had gone past. Ever since that terrible night's experience Weemullee's eyes have remained large and round.

The Emu and the Crow

The emu and the crow were man and wife, and lived in a gurli, or hut. One very wet day they remained indoors, and the emu, who always had the habit of kicking his legs about, lay on his back on the floor to pass the time, and kept kicking at the roof. After a while he struck a weak spot, and made a hole, through which the rain beat into the gurli.

The emu was too lazy to go and repair the damage, but sent the crow, his wife, out in the wet to patch the hole in the roof. The emu kept on with his play of kicking upward, and soon made another hole in the roof, which again the crow had to go out and repair.

This went on for some time till the crow became angry, and taking a piece of bark, scooped up some hot coals from the fire, and threw them on the emu's chest, as he lay on his back amusing himself by kicking at the roof of the gurli.

The hot coals burnt his breast so severely that even to the present time there is a callous, dark patch on the breast of a cock emu. Moreover, emus continue the old habit of kicking upwards with their legs when they are rolling themselves in the sand or elsewhere to clean their feathers.

55

The Cave of Byama

A man named Yoo-nee-a-ra, the chief of the Kamilaroi tribe whose country was on the Boomi River, New South Wales, once decided on going away towards the setting sun to the home of their ancestor, Byama.

He journeyed on, carrying his weapons with him, and hunting as he went. After he had travelled for several days, still going towards the sunset, he came to a place where a tribe of blackfellows lived who had the body of a man and the legs and feet of an emu. They never went about singly, but in little mobs, and lived on grubs. Their main occupation was making boomerangs out of the gidyer tree, the wood of which had a strong scent.

It is said of these emu-men that if they succeed in touching a man's feet, they will be changed into emu's feet, like their own.

When these people saw Yoo-nee-a-ra, they came up to him. They wanted to touch his feet. Yoo-nee-a-ra, having heard that there were no bandicoots in that part of the country, had brought a live one with him in his dilly-bag. When the emu-men were very close to him, he let the bandicoot go, and it ran away through the grass.

All the emu-people ran after this strange, unknown animal, and Yoo-nee-a-ra was able to escape from them.

He passed safely through the country of the emu-people, and came to a large plain where he met another tribe. These people were half men and half roly-poly. When they were facing you they looked like men, but when they turned their backs they looked like roly-polys.

This tribe asked the traveller where he was going, and he answered, 'To see Byama.'

They invited him to stay and rest himself and tried to persuade him from going any further, but he still went on. He could hear the emu-men calling after him to come back, but he took no notice of them.

After a while he came to a place where the March flies and mosquitoes were very bad, and much larger than he had ever seen before. He beat them off as best he could with a bush he carried in his hand. These insects tormented him so much that he did not know what to do. He sat down near a waterhole and made a fire.

He began to think whether he would go on, or turn back. He thought of different ways of protecting himself from these pests, and at last decided to strip a piece of bark the length of himself, and large enough to go all round his body.

He cut two holes in the bark for his eyes, and then tied bushes round his ankles and round his head, and doubled the sheet of bark around his body.

He now went on, and got through this country. Then he took his armour of bark off and put it in a waterhole to keep it soft, so that he could use it again on his return journey.

He next came to a place where there were a number of clear waterholes, in which he could see some small men walking about under the water. They kept calling out to each other, 'Thalammed? Thalammed?' which in the Kamilaroi language

means, 'Where are you?' These men were catching fish, which they threw out upon the bank.

The traveller went on, and after a time came to a camp where there were two old women. These women were of giant size, and had no men with them. They lived on yams and the lizards known as 'shingle-backs'. They used a very small smouldering fire, so that no one could find their camping place at night.

Some distance further on, Yoo-nee-a-ra came to the edge of a large boggy marsh which seemed to stop all further travelling. After looking around the shore for a crossing-place, he saw what seemed to be a very long log, the trunk of a fallen tree, lying across the swamp and almost buried in mire.

He went along this log, which was very narrow, until he got clear of the boggy ground. By and by he came to a place where there was a large rock, under one side of which was a hollowed-out place like a cave, in which he could see Byama lying down asleep.

Byama was an old man of giant size, much larger than the blackfellows of the present time. One of Byama's daughters was sitting at a fire in front of the cave, roasting a carpet snake on the coals. She gave the traveller some food.

The country all round the rock, in which was Byama's cave, was covered with tall green trees, all leaning towards the rock and containing the nests of many birds. There was plenty of grass and saltbush growing everywhere, through which the traveller could see game of different kinds running about.

A little way in front of the cave a stream of water ran along in a hollow channel and at a short distance down this watercourse was a deep lagoon, with rocky banks at one end and reeds at the other, covered with swans, ducks and other waterfowl.

The visitor, after having refreshed himself and had a short rest at the fire of Byama's daughter, started homewards. He again went through the same places and saw the same people as he had passed on the journey out.

Shortly after his return to his own country, he took ill and died, perhaps because of the evil powers of some of the queer people he had seen on the way.

This is why no other blackfellows will make the journey to the land of Byama.

How the Kamilaroi
Obtained Fire

At one time the crow was the only man who had fire. When the other people had been eating game, blood was always seen around their mouths and jaws, but nothing of that kind was ever noticed about the crow's face. When he was questioned about this he said he always cut his meat into small pieces with his stone knife, but the people did not believe this was the true answer.

They invited the crow to a corroboree where some comical fellows were to dance. After a number of clever dancers had taken their turn, without making the crow amused, the shingle-back and sleepy-lizard danced along by the campfires, singing:

Yamburngain bumbaingo nyi dhu-u-ra
Gunaga bid-yeringga bumbul guna-guna

All the time they were dancing, the ordure was trickling down their legs, and when they gave a special jump there was an extra discharge of it.

This so took the crow's attention that the sparrow-hawk, Gur-gur, came up beside him, catching hold of the little bag containing the fire, and running away with it.

When the crow saw what had happened, he rushed after Gur-gur, and in the scuffle the fire got jerked out of the bag, setting alight the dry grass and leaves. The crow tried his best to stop the fire from getting away by stamping upon it with his feet, and when that did not put it out he lay down full length and rolled over and over among the burning grass, but all his attempts to get the fire back failed.

Fire spread through the whole country, so that all the people had their share of it, and have used it ever since.

The crow got so black by rolling in the burnt grass that he has kept that colour to the present day. The whitish rings round a crow's eyes show where his skin was scorched. [Most of my Australian readers will know that when a blackfellow is burnt severely, a white patch usually remains where the skin was injured.]

59

The Dingo-Man
and the Maccassars

The dingo-man Barwal and his wife the dingo-woman Durandurar sat down in a country at Buckingham Bay. The dingo-woman talked: 'My husband, you must cut paperbark and make a canoe.' Barwal cut bark and made a canoe. He and his wife began to carry it to the distant salt water. On the way, their children were born. They put the children in the canoe and together they carried the canoe on their heads.

The dingo-woman talked: 'You and I cannot rest. We must carry this canoe right up to the beach.'

At last Barwal said, 'My head is sore. We will have a rest.' They put the canoe on the ground and tied it up to an ironwood tree. In the morning they carried the canoe on to the salt water.

The canoe was getting heavy. They carried the canoe on and came out at a beach. Far up the beach was a camp of Maccassars. 'What are we going to do now?' asked Barwal.

'Come on,' said his wife. 'We will put this canoe in the salt water.'

'Look,' said Barwal, 'there is another big camp of Maccassars over there on the headland. This is the place of the crocodile dreaming. This country belongs to you and me.'

Barwal and his wife lowered the canoe into the salt water. They got into the canoe with their children and pushed off from the beach. The canoe shot forward out into the salt water. It shot out and down. Down the canoe went into the salt water taking the children with it. Only Barwal and his wife got back to the beach. They sat down on the beach and howled for their children.

Two big stones sit down on the beach at that place. Barwal and his wife talked: 'These stones are our bodies. Our spirits go on to another place.'

Barwal and his wife were hungry. They walked up to the camp of the Maccassars and asked for food. The Maccassars said, 'You can go and see the old man, Yoortjing. He might give you tucker.

Barwal and his wife walked up to the camp of Yoortjing, the boss of the Maccassars. A lot of tribesmen were camped there and their children were playing about. The Maccassar saw Barwal and his wife coming along the beach. He got two blankets and spread them out. He called to Barwal and his wife to come up.

Barwal asked, 'Why do you make beds?'

'Why,' said the Maccassar, 'you two are my friends. I would like you to sit down here.' The Maccassar called Barwal 'Grandfather'. He wanted to give Barwal the blankets. He asked Barwal if he wanted a pillow.

Barwal answered, 'No.'

'Well then,' said the Maccassar, 'what about this meat?'

'Is it cooked?' asked Barwal.

'Yes,' said the Maccassar.

'Then I don't want it,' said Barwal.

'You want raw meat?' the Maccassar asked.

'Yes, raw meat,' said Barwal.

The Maccassar gave Barwal and his wife raw meat and the dingo-man and his wife sat down on the beach and ate the meat raw.

Then the Maccassar asked, 'Do you want to come inside my house?'

'No,' said Barwal. 'We are going to sleep in the grass.'

'But there is a big rain coming on,' said the Maccassar.

'No matter,' said Barwal. 'You see that rock and that ant-bed? That is where I and my wife will sleep. This is my country. It is better that you go back to your country. You see that fire a long way off in the country Yoormanga? That is your country. It is better that you load your boat with all your things. Pull down this house and take everything back to your country.'

Then the Maccassar said, 'You are angry with me, Barwal. I will give you blankets and tucker. Are you still angry?'

'Yes, I am still angry,' said Barwal.

Then the Maccassar said, 'Look, Barwal, you and I can sit down as one company.'

'No,' answered Barwal. 'This is my country. It is better that you go back to your own country.'

The Maccassars loaded up their boat. The dingo-man sat down and watched them. 'Pull up everything you have made,' said the dingo-man. 'Pull up the bamboo you have planted. Pull up your garden. Take everything. Take your iron, your nails with you. You see that smoke? You go there. You stop in that country always. This is my country.'

Barwal and his wife sat down on the beach and watched the Maccassars loading the boat. They watched them pulling on the ropes to haul up the sails. The Maccassars took their wives and children into the boat. Yoortjing the Maccassar had told all the other Maccassar boats and as the Maccassars pulled up the anchors and the wind filled the sails and the fleet sailed away, Barwal called, 'Go back to your country and stay there. This is my country. I sit down here.'

The Two Brothers

Two brothers made a bark canoe in the country at Milingimbi. They carried the canoe down to the salt water. The elder brother stood up in the front of the canoe looking out with his fish spear. He speared a barramundi, heaved it out of the water, and swung it into the canoe.

The elder brother speared catfish and mullet. 'We have plenty of fish now,' said his brother.

'Yes,' said the elder brother, 'we have wives and a lot of children too.'

The brothers turned the canoe into the mouth of a creek. The elder brother speared a stingray. He looked out and speared a barramundi. Then, as the brothers paddled the canoe, laden with fish, up the creek, the big snake, Kurrijarra, humped up out of the water. The elder brother stood ready with his spear. The head of the snake rose up and the brother struck him at the back of the head with his spear. Lightning zigzagged out of the sky. The big snake thrashed the water, and his tongue was like a whip. In one lunge and gulp the snake seized and swallowed the canoe, the fish and the two men.

The snake sank down under the water. He travelled underneath the ground. 'This is the saltwater country,' the snake said. 'I will go another way to a freshwater country.'

The snake came up out of the ground blowing out spray and making a rainbow. He stood up and looked around at the country. 'I think I must have swallowed my own countrymen,' he talked. The snake was belching and breathing hard. He lay down and heaved, and brought out the first brother. Again he heaved, and the second brother was vomited out. The snake kept the canoe and the fish inside him. 'The canoe and the fish are mine,' he said. 'Only these men I bring out.'

The snake nosed one of the brothers along and out into the sun. He nosed the second brother into the sun alongside him. Then the snake drew back and lay down some distance away and watched.

The brothers were asleep. Soon, the hot sun dried their bodies. The white-ants came up and began to drink at the blood in their veins. The next time the ants came up and bit, the brothers flinched and kicked. The younger brother sat up. Then the elder brother got up and looked around. 'Oh, brother,' he cried, 'what country is this?'

'I don't know it,' the younger brother said.

'Ah,' said the elder brother, 'this country is our destiny, our dreaming.'

The big snake was watching the two brothers. 'Oh my countrymen,' he said to himself, 'poor fellows. They have awakened in this place where I have brought them. This is their country now.'

The Corroboree of Naarait

In the Dreamtime, tribesmen were lying asleep in the sand of a riverbed. A flock of white cockatoos came circling and screaming round the tops of the paperbark trees. One tribesman awoke and sat looking up at them. As he did so, one cockatoo came circling and screaming lower down towards him.

The tribesman said, 'I can catch that song so that I can sing it, and play it on the drone-pipe.'

The cockatoo perched on a bough above the tribesman and began calling and talking down to him.

The white cockatoo said, 'I am Naarait, and I will tell you how to make a new corroboree.'

'You must get plenty of young girls, plenty of young men, and plenty of men who can make the dances. And you must paint them with white stripes down the centre of their faces, and white stripes going past their cheek-bones. And you must paint their arms and legs and chests. And you must put white feathers in their hair.

Naarait said, 'This is how you must make the song of Naarait.' He began calling and screaming down from the bough of the paperbark tree.

Naarait began to dance on the bough, calling out, 'You must dance sideways like this, and look this way, and this way, and you must cry like this.'

Naarait told the tribesman that he must sing up all the tribes to this corroboree of the white cockatoo.

And then Naarait told the tribesman what kind of drone-pipe to use, and how the sticks and the bones should be played. And Naarait danced on the bough, and threw out his yellow crest, and then flew screaming away up through the paperbark trees.

When the tribesmen awoke, the first tribesman told them of the corroboree he had learned. With the song-sticks, he sang to them the song of Naarait. The song tells how the white cockatoo lives in the desert and finds water in the forks and big knots of the trees. And the song said that the tribesmen too could find water in the desert trees.

Then these tribesmen of the Rembarunga tribe made the corroboree of Naarait. They made it with many young girls and young men, with many dancers and singers, with playing on the bamboo drone-pipe, with boomerangs quivered together, with song-sticks and bones.

This is a corroboree which starts and travels along the river to the different tribes, that turns and travels in another direction, that travels on to other tribes, and finishes when another corroboree is ready to start up and begin travelling.

Brolga and Jabiru

In the Dreamtime, two tribesmen, Janaran, the jabiru, and Bonorong, the brolga, met at a billabong.

'What are you going to do?' asked Janaran.

'I'm going to look out for lily roots, and I want to be able to fly,' said Bonorong.

'Well,' said Janaran, 'I'm going to look out for fish, and I want to be able to fly, too.'

'But how are we going to do this?' asked Bonorong.

'Why,' said Janaran, 'we'll have to make ourselves feathers. I'm going to have white feathers with green and black bands down my wings. I'll have a dark blue neck and head, and I'll have red-yellow legs.'

When he said this, he began to dance. He held out his arms like outspread wings and cried out, 'Klock, klock, klock, ker-luk.' He ran along the ground with his arms beating like wings and began to fly up through the trees.

Janaran circled the tops of some high paperbark trees and then came gliding down to rest in front of Bonorong. He closed his wings. 'Klock, klock,' he said, strutting about. 'Do you see my feathers, and how I can fly?'

'Yes, yes,' cried Bonorong. 'I'm going to make feathers now. I'll be blue-grey, with a grey breast. I'll have red on the sides of my head, and I'll have yellow legs.' Then Bonorong held out his arms like outspread wings and began to dance.

'Arr-arr-arr, preek-preek-eek-eek-preek,' he sang out. He too ran along the ground with his arms outspread like wings and flew away high over the trees and the wide plain beyond. Then he circled and came gliding in to rest and fold his wings in front of Janaran.

'Now I've got feathers!' cried Bonorong as he stood on his toes and stretched his neck and flapped his wings. 'Now that I can fly,' he cried, 'I'm going over the plains to find a dry billabong where there are lily-roots.'

'Yes, that's right,' said Janaran. 'You have to look out for lily-roots, and I have to look out for fish.'

Then Bonorong opened his wings and flew off through the trees. 'Bo-bo' (Good-bye), he called as he flew away.

'Bo-bo, cumwun' (Good-bye, friend), called back Janaran.

Then Janaran stepped down into the shallows of the billabong and started wading and looking out for fish. And as he waded he sang this song to himself:

'Kadji-ooruk kalinee, kadji-ooruk kalinee, kadji-ooruk kalinee, ar-kanar, woo-rukee, kadji-ooruk woorukee. Kut!'

This song means, 'I see fish darting this way, and fish darting that way. Here's one I can spear. Kut!' This is the sound his bill makes in the water as he spears a fish.

This is the song of Janaran, one of the songs that are sung to the bamboo drone-pipe in the Djauan tribe.

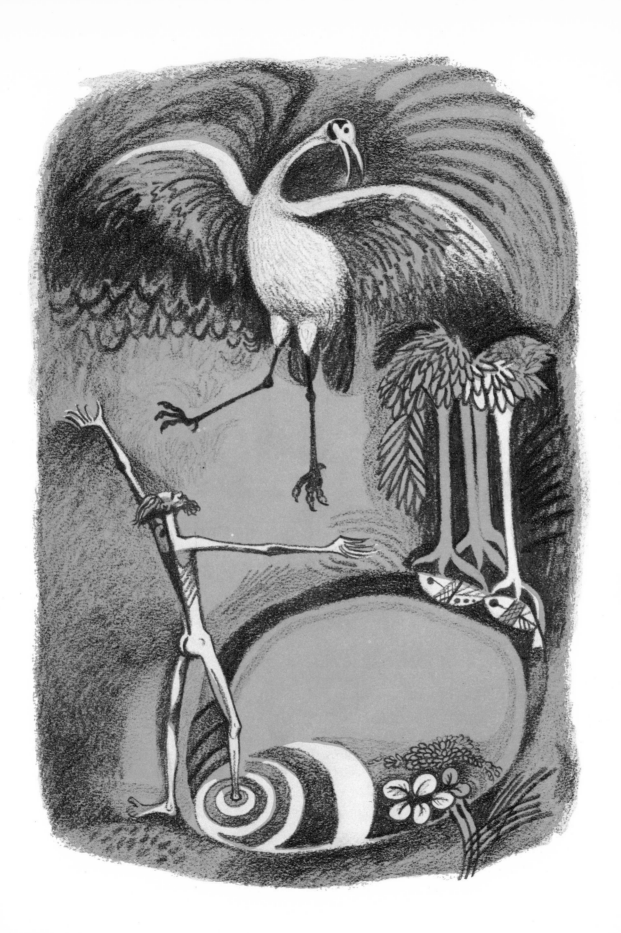

A Little Boy Crying

In the Dreamtime a tribe was camped at a place which the white man calls Pagan Swamp on the Roper River.

A little boy belonging to this tribe was crying all the time for some goanna tail. He could not be quietened and the tribesmen and the lubras would pick up a piece of kangaroo tail or the wing of a flying fox and say, 'What about this?' But the little boy would only take it, throw it away, and start crying again.

A long way off, the black rock-snake was travelling. She would go down underground, and then come out and travel above the ground. Once, when the black rock-snake came out of the ground, she stopped and listened.

She heard a child crying somewhere. She went on in the direction of the crying and then went down into the ground again.

The black rock-snake came up again. She listened. She heard the crying and went underground again, travelling to where the sound came from.

In the camp, the little boy was still throwing away any food that was given to him and breaking out into crying all the time.

Suddenly, out of the ground, came the head and body of the great black rock-snake. Her tongue was shooting out lightning and her mouth opened showing her fangs. Her great body lashed out far across the swamp and, as she drew herself out of the ground, a huge force of water rushed out after her. The water filled the hollow of the swamp where the tribe was camped, and drowned them all.

Then the black rock-snake went on her way to Moorinjairee, the place where the Dreamtime ended. This is the place which the white man calls Newcastle Waters.

Dooruk the Emu

Ongi was sitting under a big fig tree on the bank of the billabong. He was painting his spear-blade with red ochre and white clay in a cross-hatched design. He asked me if I had noticed that the plum tree, called Woial, was beginning to flower.

'When the plum tree comes into flower,' said Ongi, 'we know that the rain-time is close up. Soon, Dooruk, the emu, will come looking for plums. He comes to the plum tree and kicks the trunk with his foot. The plums fall down in showers and Dooruk runs about under the tree pecking them up. He makes this drumming sound in his chest, "duk-duk-duk".

'A man comes and finds one tree that Dooruk always comes to after the plums. He sees the emu's tracks all round the tree. In the night he climbs into the tree with his spear and club. He sits in the boughs and leaves waiting for Dooruk.

'The tribesmen have been hunting Dooruk in the rain-time and this has made the emu frightened. In the "little-bit" daylight Dooruk comes looking for the plums. The man in the tree keeps still. He hears the emu as he walks around, out from the tree. "Duk-duk" he says now and again. Dooruk is hungry for the plums, but he thinks that someone may be hiding in the tree, waiting to spear him.

'The tree is quiet. Dooruk can see the plums lying on the ground underneath the tree. He walks around closer and closer, craning his neck and peering under the tree with his red eyes.

'At last Dooruk waits no longer. The tree is dark and quiet. Suddenly he runs right in underneath the boughs. "Duk-duk-duk" he says as he walks about pecking up the plums.

'The man in the tree has his spear hooked up in his womerah. Without touching a leaf he draws back his arm with the spear and the spear-thrower. He knows where he must spear Dooruk, in the thigh joint, cutting the big sinew.

'He waits. He watches Dooruk. Suddenly the spear hurtles down out of the boughs. It finds Dooruk's thigh joint, cuts the sinew.

'Dooruk falls to the ground. He flounders about, crying out with guttural cries. He is beating his wings, trying to get up. The man drops down out of the tree with his club. Dooruk strikes at him with his long neck and strong beak. The man dodges the striking head. He runs in and clubs Dooruk behind his angry red eyes. Dooruk tries to rear up. His wings beat the air. He falls down. His body shudders. He stiffens out on the ground and shakes his feet.

'That is how we must hunt the emu in the rain-time,' said Ongi as he made with his sliver of bark the last, delicate line of white clay down his spear-blade.

The Lyre Bird

Long, long ago a blackfellow, leaving his two wives and his little girl at his camp, went hunting. While he was away another blackfellow, who had been watching for his chance, came within sight of the camp.

The wives saw this stranger, and so that he would not camp too near them they sent the little girl with a light to make a fire for him where he was.

At first he seemed very grateful, but presently pretended that the ants annoyed him, so that he could get no rest, so the girl moved the fire a little nearer to her mother's camp. First by one excuse, and then another, he got his fire moved nearer, and nearer, until he was quite close to the women's camp.

Watching his chance he sprang upon the two women, and with his waddy knocked them senseless. He then took them away to his camp which was in a very deep opening in a steep mountain. There was no water there, yet he kept them strictly prisoners.

Each time he went away hunting he drew after him a rope of twisted vines which was fastened to a stringy bark tree at the top of the cliff.

In their rocky prison the two women were kept and cruelly treated. Sometimes he kept them for days without water, then when they were almost mad with thirst he offered them a loathsome draught.

This treatment made them watch for a chance to escape. At last it came. The man forgot to draw up his ladder after him. The two women used it to get to the top, where they hid themselves in the scrub until the blackfellow returned. As soon as he had gone down to his camp they drew up the rope, leaving him with no means of escape.

He begged them to let down the rope, but they only taunted him all the time, talking as hard as they could at him.

When they last saw him he was frantically scraping up and scratching together little heaps of sticks and stones, uttering all the time most doleful cries.

Cries which are heard today in the sweet notes of the Lyrebird, whose haunts are in those Southern Mountains, for it was into a Lyre Bird this blackfellow was changed.

And the Aborigines say they have seen his old camp in a range on the south bank of the Moruya, between Wambean and Kulwarry.

Murgah Muggui

The Spider

Murgah Muggui was a bunna, or cannibal, and lived by herself in a pine-tree scrub. She was a great wirreenun, or witch. This was the way she gained the victims she desired for food. When she saw a young man going hunting through the bush she would change herself from an ugly old witch into a beautiful young woman. Then she would go towards the young man and ask him where he was going.

'Hunting,' he would say, upon hearing that she proposed to accompany him, and off they would go together.

When they came back she would suggest, 'It is late; you had better camp with me tonight.'

'No,' he would say. 'I have a wife. I must get back to her with some food.'

'Well, just wait while I cook a little bit for you to eat before you go.'

The man, feeling hungry, would agree to this. Having eaten he would feel disinclined to move, especially when the beautiful young woman begged him to stay, telling him he could easily say to his wife that he had camped in the bush, and she would never know he had not camped alone. He might stay one night with her when she was lonely, she said. She had her way—he stayed. When he was soundly asleep Murgah Muggui stole away from her fireside, picked up her gunnai, or yamstick, which was very sharply pointed at the end, and stole back with it to the sleeping man.

He opened his eyes and saw before him an old woman, with her gunnai poised to strike him. His surprise was so great at seeing a hideous old hag that he lay paralysed as down came the gunnai, which pinned him dead to the earth.

So gained Murgah Muggui many victims on whose remains she feasted.

One day Mullyan, the strong and clever man of the tribe came that way. He saw a beautiful young woman, who advanced towards him. She asked him what she had asked the others, with him went hunting, and persuaded him as she had them, to camp the night there.

But Mullyan was suspicious of her—he only feigned sleep. He saw the beautiful young woman steal away: he saw her pick up her gunnai, and as she did so turn into a hideous old witch, who, with a leer of triumph came stealthily towards him. Down came the gunnai, but before it touched his body he had seized it. He jumped up, pulled the gunnai from the grasp of the astonished old hag, turned it upon her, and drove it through her heart, killing her on the spot where so many had fallen victims to her.

Her spirit was turned into Murgah Muggui, the spider, who lives on the pine ridges, where she spins her fine web traps from tree to tree, devouring, as of old, her many victims caught within the gold and silver meshes she makes so cunningly.

69

Billai

The Crimson-Wing Parrot

Though Billai had been promised to Gubbee, she herself had chosen another. Gubbee was old; her lover was young; she vowed that she would never be Gubbee's, but her mother said she was promised, and to the dardurr, or camp, of Gubbee she must go.

In vain Billai protested, but before the time for going to the hated dardurr came, she saw one day her lover, and told him that on the morrow she was to be given to Gubbee for ever.

'Have courage,' he said. 'Say no more to your mother, or anyone. But tonight, when all sleep, steal from the camp, and together we will fly to a far country, where Gubbee will not follow us. I will go now as if to hunt, telling all that I shall not return tonight. No one will watch you. You can steal away to join me before the moon rises. We will hide together until Bahloo the Moon looks down at us, and then by his light we will put scrubs between us and the camp.'

When night came, and all were asleep, Billai stole from the camp away to the meeting place, where she knew her lover awaited her. When she reached him she was too frightened of pursuit to pause for the rising of the moon, so onward together they sped; on all through that night and with but short pauses the next day.

At night they reached a big river, and finding there was a canoe, they crossed the river in it; then they felt safe, with the river between them and probable pursuers, and no canoe on the other side. With light hearts at the thought of their escape they sat down to eat. As they were eating a storm arose; the wind howled round their rough shelter, the thunder roared over them, and the lightning flashed around them. Billai trembled with fear; she was afraid the spirits had sent this storm to kill her for running away from Gubbee, who was a great wirreenun, or wizard, but her lover said the spirits had sent the storm but to wash out their tracks. Even as he was speaking came a terrific clap of thunder, and a flash of almost instantaneous lightning, that showed them plainly to eyes, gleaming with hatred, that were peering through the darkness for them.

'We shall be killed,' said Billai. 'Doongairah the lightning will strike us.'

'Not so,' said her lover. 'Did not our mothers put the ice the Meamei sent down under our arms and between our joints? Are not those to whom that has been done safe from flashes of Doongairah? So have our mothers told us ever.'

But Billai clung to him trembling. And well might she tremble, for even now, waiting for another flash to lighten the darkness, stood Gubbee, meaning to slay with his spear her lover, and take her back to his dardurr.

Billai shut her eyes as the flash came, and did not see the blow fall which knocked lifeless her loved one. Scarcely had she realized that an enemy was there before she found herself seized and held by Gubbee. She could not free herself from his powerful grasp, and he held her until the storm was passed and the moon shone out again. Then spurning with his foot the lifeless body of his rival, back to camp he started, with Billai

his captive. She wailed and cried aloud unceasingly, until at length he grew so angry he gave her a knock with a nullah nullah, which silenced her, and she was senseless to all that followed for many hours, until she came to, finding herself in Gubbee's dardurr, with him sleeping beside her. She stole from the camp to the nearest dheal tree, the sacred tree of her tribe. She broke twigs from it, and tied them around her wrists, her elbows, her ankles, her knees, her waist and neck, and a small twig she stuck through the hole in the cartilage of her nose. Then taking her stone knife she cut her forehead and shoulders until the blood streamed down both arms, as she sang a death wail for her lover.

Her wailing wakened Gubbee, and he came fiercely towards her. 'How dares my wife,' he asked, 'to sing a widow's wail for another man?'

'Not your wife am I, but the widow of my loved one, he whom you murdered.' And louder and louder wailed Billai, calling on her loved one's name, which she knew would bring the spirit of the dead to her. It is for that reason that all names of the dead are taboo.

Angrier grew Gubbee as he heard her ceaseless wailing for his rival. He strode towards her, and said, 'Strip those dheal twigs from you. Cease mourning for my enemy, and hasten back with me to my dardurr.'

'Kill me rather,' said Billai, as the blood flowed afresh down her arms, staining the green leaves she had bound on them.

'I shall not kill you, for then would your spirit join his. You shall live, and live as my wife. Even now I have come to take you to my dardurr. You shall know that to me only do you belong,' and he stretched out his hand to clutch her. But even as he did so she slipped away. No longer was a woman before him; from where she had stood flew a green parrot with crimson wings. To this parrot the spirits said these words: 'Swiftly fly to the eastward, swiftly fly. There you will overtake the spirit of your lost love, and reach him before he gets to the holy mountain. He shall then take your new shape, and be even as you are, but brighter. Together you can roam through this country, seeing and knowing your old tribe but rearing a new one, who will be as you are now, and bear your name forever.'

Far from the baffled Gubbee flew Billai, over the grey saltbush plains, over the grey mulga scrubs, away, and away, until in the distance she saw the shadow of the sacred mountain.

'I am too late!' she shrieked, in a harsh, discordant voice, which has been the voice of her tribe ever since. But she was not too late. A spirit, hearing her cry, turned. It was her lover. She shrieked again to him to stop, and as he halted he too was changed into a crimson-wing parrot, still more brilliant in hue than Billai.

Shrieking greetings at each other in their new voices, back they flew joyously to their old country, seeing there their tribes, who knew them not, deeming them only birds of rare plumage come from a far country. But Gubbee knew them, and when he saw them he cried, 'It is Billai!' and he told how she had escaped him.

Ever since these crimson-winged parrots have been known as 'The Billai'.

The Bunyee Bunyee
or Bunyip

For a long time the blackfellows were puzzled to know what had become of many young men of their tribes, who had at various times gone out hunting alone and never returned. They could track these men to the edges of a large lagoon, but there the tracks would disappear. There arose among them such a dread of this lagoon that they became too frightened to fish there, or to try and catch any of the game that abounded on and around it. They felt sure that there must be kurreahs, or crocodiles, in that water.

One old wizard said he was not frightened of any kurreah. He would take his weapons and find out the mystery of that lagoon. He tracked the last young man who had disappeared to the edge of the water. Keeping a lookout, he soon saw a ripple on the smooth surface. It widened and widened until, in front of the first ripple showed out a huge crocodile coming straight towards the wizard, who prepared to defend himself. One after another he hurled his weapons at the monster, who, however, as if they were mere straws blown on him by the wind, still came on, writhing as he left the water, forming, as he went along, a channel across the dry land.

The wizard now began to fear he had been too daring, for the crocodile gained on him. His weapons were all gone, and he was getting exhausted, yet closer and closer wriggled on the kurreah. The wizard doubled on his tracks and tried to dodge the monster, but it was no use. On came the crocodile forming watercourses as he went.

The wizard gave a last despairing look around for help, or refuge. He saw an immense bumble-tree. Hope spurred him on, for he remembered that bumbles were the mothers-in-law of the kurreahs. That no man may approach or speak to his mother-in-law is the rule of all the tribes.

He was saved! With a final effort he reached the tree, and sank exhausted in the shade.

Baffled of his prey, the kurreah lashed around in a fury, forming as he did so a large waterhole, in which he turned and retraced his way to the lagoon, and so the wizard escaped. But he was still determined to solve the mystery, which the appearance of the kurreah, or crocodile, did not explain, for the tracks he had seen belonged neither to man nor kurreah.

On his return to his camp he consulted his sacred crystal. In it he saw the missing men imprisoned in a cave on the side of the lagoon, guarded by strange animals, such as would make the tracks he had seen. He told all this to another wizard, gave him instructions to follow in his absence, then placing an extra strong yamstick in his waistband, he started off again.

As he passed the bumble-tree, he picked a bunch of it, placing some in his waistband and in the frontlet on his head. This done he had no fear of the kurreah.

73

When he reached the lagoon he plunged in for a swim. After he came out he walked along the edge where he had seen the strange tracks. He had not been there long when out from the water came two animals like none he had seen before. They were about four times the size of the biggest dogs, were covered with grey hair, had four feet like horses' hoofs, stumpy tails, and teeth like a dog, except they only had one tooth on each side of their mouths, like boars' tusks. These animals were called bunyee bunyees.

These two animals tried to round him back into the water, but he ran along, keeping close to the bank, where he still saw the tracks of his missing friends. Along he went at a good swinging pace, the animals after him.

At the far side of the lagoon towards which the tracks seemed to be leading was a high bank. The bunyee bunyees drove him round to this, over it into the lagoon. At the bottom of the bank was an opening, through which they drove him. Then, on through some water, up an incline to dry ground, and through another opening into a dry cave which was between two and three hundred yards long. Having driven him to the cave by just touching him with their tusks, the bunyee bunyees turned and left him.

He had solved the mystery; there before him were the missing men of his tribe. Hopeless of rescue, they merely regarded him as one more victim, and so scarcely looked at him.

The wizard looked round the cave. He saw skeletons on the floor. On the sides of the cave were carvings and drawings. In one instance, in a whole series of scenes, was roughly shown the pursuit of a man by two animals, the bunyee bunyees. The man was next shown falling over a precipice, then sitting down dejectedly as were the living men now.

Further on he saw outlines of emus and other birds, various animals and fish, men's hands, and other marks. Some were hewn out of stone, others but surface drawings. One or two of them were coloured, but the rest were merely outlined in white.

Clutching his yamstick, the wizard advanced towards the men who were lying about. Touching his stick, he said, 'With the help of this I shall save you all.' They looked doubtfully at him, though some recognized him as a noted wizard.

He went on, 'I told another wizard that if I did not get back in a certain time to follow my tracks; he and the strongest of the tribe. Should my tracks go over the edge of the bank, he was to go over all the surrounding ground for some distance, listening along its surface. I suspected these bunyee bunyees, of whom there are legends, had a cave somewhere here.' He would not tell these men of his crystal vision, but went on, 'I thought they might have you imprisoned, as according to legend they do not eat men. If I were right I should be put in a cave and find you all there, kept alive by water and fruit of the budthen brought to you by the bunyee bunyees, who, I had heard, each time they fed their prisoners counted them, not as we count, but by smelling to find out if one is away.

'I knew I should not be hurt; if they catch one escaping they will touch him with their side teeth; that stops him. I told the other wizard that if I discovered a cave I should tap the roof with my stick until he heard it, and where they heard this tapping they were to dig a hole big enough for a man to get through. They were to get a tree

ladder ready, a tree trunk with steps cut into it. As soon as the hole was made, this ladder was to be slipped down, so that we might all climb it and escape.'

Up jumped the prisoners and asked that the tapping might begin at once.

Choosing the highest part of the cave the wizard began. He warned them that there might be some delay as he had told the other wizard to be careful to come when the wind was blowing off the lagoon, in case the bunyee bunyees smelt them and upset their plan, for sooner than let them escape the bunyee bunyees would give them to the kurreah, who would kill them.

The wind must have been favourable, for it was not long before the tapping of the yamstick was answered by a sharp quick sound like digging.

Anxiously the prisoners waited, straining their eyes upward. At last a ray of light came through. The blackfellows above worked on until the opening was large enough, then they slipped the ladder down. There was a rush for it, but the wizard told them to go one at a time in case they broke it. He himself waited until the last. Just as he stepped on to the ladder, he heard a splash in the water. The bunyee bunyees were coming!

They smelt that their prisoners were gone. They bounded forward. The wizard was nearly up the ladder. One bunyee bunyee leapt up to seize him, just touched his foot and fell back. Before he could bound up again, the wizard was above ground and the ladder gone.

There was great rejoicing in the camp when the long-lost men returned, but the wizards were not content. They did not like being cut off from the supply of fish and game abounding in the lagoon. They had a meeting and decided by their magic to dry off the water, then both the bunyee bunyees and kurreahs would have to go or perish. So they put their rain stones in the fire and sang their drought songs until all the water was dried up.

Bones of kurreahs that died were to be seen for ages in the watercourses.

But no bones of the bunyee bunyees were ever found, so these animals must have escaped alive, and from time to time they are still heard of in various lagoons.

Afterwards the wizards took their rain stones out of their fires and put them in water, sang their rain songs and so made a great rain which refilled the lagoon, which has never been empty since. And its water is still a favourite camping ground for blackfellows in search of game and fish which abound in it, as in the time when it was haunted by the bunyee bunyees.

Yaraandoo

A Kamilaroi Legend of the Southern Cross

In the very beginning when Byamee, the Sky King, walked the earth, out of the red ground of the ridges he made two men and a woman. When he saw that they were alive he showed them such plants as they should eat to keep life, then he went on his way.

For some time they lived on such plants as he had shown them, then came a drought, and plants grew scarce, and when one day a man killed a kangaroo rat he and the woman ate some of its flesh, but the other man would not eat though he was famished for food, and lay as one dead.

Again and again the woman told him it was good and pressed him to eat.

Exasperated, weak as he was, he rose and walked angrily away towards the sunset, while the other two still ate hungrily.

When they had finished they looked for him, found he had gone some distance, and went after him. Over the sandhills, over the pebbly ridges they went, losing sight of him from time to time. When they reached the edge of the coolibah plain they saw on the other side, by the river, their mate. They called to him to stop, but he heeded them not. On he went until he reached a huge yaraan, or white gum-tree, beneath which he fell to the ground. As he lay there dead they saw beside him a black figure with two huge fiery eyes. This figure raised him into the tree, and dropped him into its hollow centre.

While speeding still across the plain they heard so terrific a burst of thunder that they fell startled to the ground. When they raised themselves they gazed wonderingly towards the giant gum-tree. They saw it being lifted from the earth and passing through the air towards the southern sky. They could not see their lost mate, but fiery eyes gleamed from the tree. Suddenly a raucous screaming broke the stillness; they saw it came from two yellow-crested white cockatoos flying after the vanishing tree. Mouyi they called them.

On went the Spirit Tree, after it flew the mouyi, shrieking loudly to it to stop, that they might reach their roosting place in it.

At last the tree planted itself near to the Warrambool, or Milky Way, which leads to where the Sky Gods live. When it seemed stationary the tree gradually disappeared from their sight. They only saw four fiery eyes shine out. Two were the eyes of Yowee, the Spirit of Death, the other two the eyes of the first man to die.

The mouyi fly after the tree, trying always to reach their roost again.

When all Nature realized that the passing of this man meant Death had come into the world there was wailing everywhere. The swamp oak trees sighed incessantly, the gum-tree shed tears of blood, which crystallized as red gum.

To this day to the tribes of that part is the Southern Cross known as 'Yaraandoo' —the place of the White Gum-tree—and the Pointers as Mouyi, the white cockatoos.

So is the first coming of Death remembered by the tribe, to whom the Southern Cross is a *memento mori*.

Melapi

We have always believed that people lived after death. We call the spirit of a man pangari (which means shadow).

The old people often talk about where the spirit of a man has gone to after it has left the body. They say that it goes westward to Nurunderi.

We also believe in other spirits who walk about the earth and who can make themselves seen or unseen as they like. There is Nalkaru, a terrible spirit who seeks to kill people. And there is Melapi, who is always lying in wait for men.

Have any of us ever seen these spirits?

Yes. I have heard our old men say they have. My father saw Melapi once. He was sure that he had. And this is the way it happened.

My father had gone into the reeds to snare ducks. He took with him a long rod, with a noose at the end. He had patiently sat at the edge of the swamp until the ducks came. At last one got within reach so he let the noose fall over its head and then suddenly dragged it out.

This frightened the rest of the flock, so he got up and came away. He walked in a track through the high, thick reeds which were far above his head, and then came to a place where they were lower—about up to his waist.

Suddenly he heard the whirr of a waddy as it flew past his head and yet he saw nothing.

He started, dropping the duck and his rod, and put up his hand to grasp a kanake out of his basket which hung from his neck down his back. He supposed some enemy had made an attack on him by flinging the waddy and was about to return it.

At that instant he felt something grapple with him, but yet saw nothing. Strong arms were put around him, and a great invisible being had him in its grasp.

He knew that Melapi sometimes thus attacked people, and that it was wisest to resist. So, though shuddering with fear, he gripped and wrestled with the spirit.

The reeds crashed and crackled under his feet as he swayed about in the struggle. He felt like a boy in the power of the mighty one, yet returned strain for strain. He felt faint with horror.

To get away seemed impossible; to yield and be dragged off was awful. He made another effort, and fancied that the spirit yielded a little. Encouraged, he put forth all his strength and tried to throw his invisible enemy. As he did so, with straining muscles and clenched teeth and staring eyes, he commenced to see a dim outline of a form like a man, and as he struggled it became plainer and plainer.

He gave a wild cry and Melapi burst from his grasp and disappeared.

My father, weak and tired, returned to the camp and told us what he ever afterwards believed, that he had wrestled with the great Melapi.

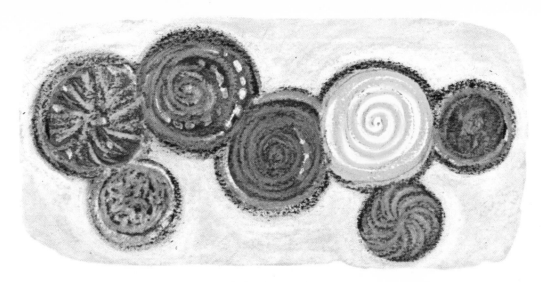

The Black Swan

Six mooras, five men and one woman (these are people who lived in the beginning), were camped. In the morning before they got up two birds came and stole their fire and flew away to the north with it.

It was very cold weather and the mooras knew that they would die of cold if they could not get a fire, so they followed the birds till night. They were then near Kandramooka Lake, and seeing that it was no use trying to catch up with the birds, they camped for the night.

As it was very cold they all lay down in a heap, the woman in the middle. In the morning all the men were dead, but the woman, through being in the middle of the heap, was alive. On seeing this she called the place *Nunku Purrini*, which means cold lie down. The moora men had turned to stone. They are there to this day.

The woman, whose name was Kuti, then went in search of a fire-stick. Going south, she saw seven girls with a fire each. The seven girls, as soon as they saw the woman Kuti, jumped up into the sky, taking their fires with them. These girls became stars which are now known as Monkira.

Kuti travelled on until she came to Lake Gregory. Here she saw an old woman, whose name was Nardoo Chilpanie, who was pounding nardoo seed. Kuti wondered how she could get fire from this old woman. First she thought of going down as a dingo, then she thought of turning into a snake, then thought of turning into a bird.

At last she decided to go down as an old woman. When she reached the fire she made a grab at it, but Nardoo Chilpanie hit her with her digging stick. Kuti threw the stick into the lake, where it formed an island. The two then fought, and all the things in the camp were knocked into the lake, and as they fell they turned into islands. At last Nardoo Chilpanie was killed.

Kuti then turned into a swan and flew away, carrying the fire-stick in her mouth. This is why all black swans have a red edging to the inside of their beaks. It is to show where Kuti burnt her mouth when carrying the fire-stick.

The Blood of Marindi

On the high bank of a dry watercourse which comes out of the Flinders Range between Parachlina and the Meadows one can see a huge red scar.

In the old days, before there were men, there lived in the valley of this watercourse a jecko-lizard. Adno-artina was his name. Every day this lizard would climb a big rock and would sing aloud so that all could hear, 'Come out and fight. Come out and fight.'

Now the big dog Marindi came past that way, and hearing the challenge, he bounded up the dry creek-bed yelling all the way, 'I am come. I am come.' Adno-artina had a look at the dog. He saw beneath his sharp pricked ears the enormous fangs. He saw the huge bulk over which waved the white tip of his tail, and the more he looked the less he liked the idea of the fight.

'I will fight you later,' he said.

'Later you will make a feast for my pups,' returned the dog as he curled himself up at the foot of the rock.

Now, like all jecko-lizards, Adno-artina sees best when it is dark. So as the sun went down he tied a hair string round the root of his tail to make him fight better, for then his courage would not run into his tail.

It was now dark. He crept to the fighting ground, and once more, 'Come out and fight!' rang out his challenge.

Marindi the dog leapt up and tried to catch Adno-artina by the back of the neck and shake the life out of him. But the lizard ran in low beneath the terrible fighting teeth. He seized the dog by the throat and hung on. In vain Marindi shook him and scratched at him with his claws. The sharp teeth sank in and in, until at last the red blood spurted out.

The blood of Marindi the dog dyed the rocks on the banks of the creek, and from this place red ochre is obtained to this day.

And from that time on all jeckoes, now but a puny race compared with Adno-artina, have a tight ring round the root of their tails.

Later, many tribes came to this place to get red ochre. Only there could the real dog's-blood ochre be obtained. Once, while a tribe was digging out the ochre, the dog's blood jumped out and smothered them beneath. It is a fact that about 1870 a landslip took place which buried several of the Aborigines. Since then the place is of evil omen and is shunned.

The Native Bear

This story of the koala, the native bear, was told by tribesmen of the Upper Yarra. They called the native bear Koob-borr and they said that he was once a little boy whose mother and father died when he was about four years old. The tribe that he was left with were not kind to him.

At one time water was scarce everywhere, and poor little Koob-borr could not get any. No person would give him any water.

On a certain day all the tribe went out to hunt, and they forgot to take little Koob-borr with them. All the people left the camp, and Koob-borr was left alone. The people had forgotten to hang up their coolamons, which were full of water, and for once Koob-borr had enough to drink.

But so that he might always have plenty, and because he was angry for the way in which the tribe had treated him, he took all the coolamons and hung them up on the boughs of a little tree. Having done this, he next brought all the water out of the creek and put it into the coolamons, and then he climbed the tree and seated himself beside them.

The tree suddenly became very large, as large as a great many trees put together, and Koob-borr sat in the tree until evening.

In the evening the tribe came back from hunting. The people were very thirsty. The day had been hot, and they had not found any water in the places where they had been. The first man who reached the camp cried out, 'My coolamon is gone!' Another man arrived and said, 'My coolamon is gone!' And they all came, and found that all the coolamons had been taken away.

They searched for them. Some went to the creek, thinking they might have been left there, but they could not find them. Then they saw that the creek was dry.

Presently, one of the men saw the huge tree. 'Ky!' he said, 'what is that?' Then they all looked and saw their coolamons hanging on the high boughs, and little Koob-borr sitting in the midst of them. 'Wah!' said one man, 'is that you? Have you any water there?'

'Yes,' replied Koob-borr, 'here I am, and I have plenty of water, but I will not give you one drop, because you would not give me any when I was nearly dying for the want of water.'

Some of the tribesmen said they would climb the tree, but they were afraid to try, because it was so high. But they were all so thirsty that two of the men started to climb the tree. Koob-borr laughed at them. He let a little water fall on them and they loosened their hold on the tree, and fell to the ground and were killed.

Another two men tried to climb to the bough where Koob-borr sat, but he treated them in the same way, and they too fell down and were killed. This went on until nearly all the men of the tribe were killed. Then men of other tribes came, and

82

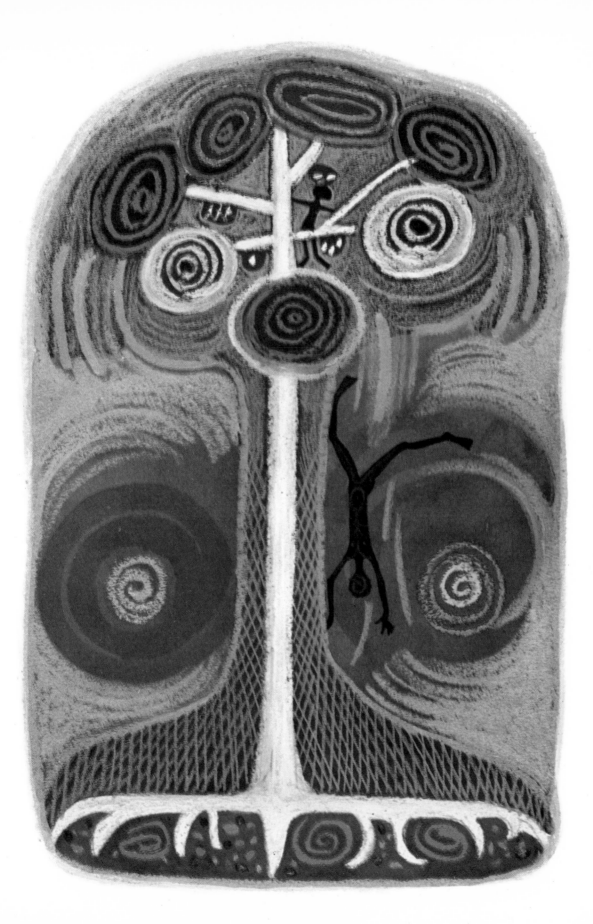

two by two they tried to climb the tree, and Koob-borr spilled water on them, and they fell down and were killed.

At last Ta-jerr and Tarrn-nin, two sons of Pund-jel, came to the camp. They had a plan for climbing the tree. They climbed round and round, just in the line which a creeping plant takes. Koob-borr laughed as he laughed at the others, until they had climbed to a great height, and then he took water and let it fall. But the men were no longer in the same place. They were higher up, and the water did not fall on them.

Koob-borr ran and got more water, and poured it where he had last seen the men, but again it did not touch them, and at last Ta-jerr and Tarrn-nin reached the high boughs. Koob-borr now began to cry, but they took no notice of his cries. They seized him and beat him until all his bones were quite soft. Then they threw him down, and the other tribesmen beat him and tried to kill him.

Koob-borr did not die. He changed to what he is now, and he ran up another tree. Ta-jerr and Tarrn-nin cut down the big tree in which all the coolamons were hung. The water came out of the tree and flowed into the creek, and there has been plenty of water ever since.

Koob-borr always keeps near the banks of creeks, and near waterholes, so that if the law is broken he may at once carry away the water. No one has roasted Koob-borr without his skin or broken his bones in killing him since the law was made.

When any one climbs a tree in which Koob-borr is sitting, he always cries in the same manner as he cried when Ta-jerr and Tarrn-nin climbed the tree and threw him down.

The Seven Sisters

On the Clarence River there once lived seven young women of the Bunjalung tribe, who were sisters. They were very clever, and had yam-sticks, in the ends of which were charms that protected the sisters from their enemies.

Every day they went out hunting for carpet snakes and always carried their yam-sticks with them. A young man named Karambal used to follow these seven sisters every day, but the sisters would not have anything to do with him.

One day Karambal suddenly came upon one of the sisters who had strayed a little away from the rest. She didn't have her yam-stick with her and Karambal carried her off to his camp.

The other sisters became very angry. They talked about the best way of rescuing their sister from Karambal, who was of the wrong kin for her to marry.

The eldest sister wanted to send a fierce storm of wind to tear up the trees by their roots, and crash them down on Karambal and kill him. The other sisters were afraid that their sister might also lose her life by the falling trees. Then one of them said that they should all go away to the west where they knew the Winter lived and bring back the frost and cold winds to punish Karambal for what he had done.

And so the sisters went away and brought the Winter, and on the place where Karambal was camped with their sister, they made the cold so severe that he almost died from the frost.

The girl he had captured did not feel this cold, because her sisters had sent her the yam-stick with the charm in its end, which she used to carry when out hunting with them.

In a short time, Karambal was glad to let the girl go back to her sisters, who were very happy to have her back with them. Then the sisters said that they would go away towards the east in search of the Summer, so as to melt the frost and ice. They did not wish to harm their tribe, but only wished to rescue their sister from Karambal.

After this trouble the seven sisters said that they would leave the earth altogether. But before doing so, they went into the mountains and made springs at the heads of all the rivers so that their people might always have plenty of water through all their hunting-grounds.

The seven sisters then went up into the sky where the faint cluster of stars which we know as the Pleiades, or the Seven Sisters, shows where they are camped.

They come into view every summer, bringing warm weather for their tribe, after which they go away slowly towards the west, where they disappear. They then send the Winter to warn their tribesmen not to carry off a woman of the wrong kin, but to choose their wives as the tribal laws say they should.

Soon after the seven sisters had left the earth, the young man Karambal looked about for another girl. This time he decided to obey the laws of his tribe. He fell in love with a young woman who belonged to the kin from which the laws said he could take a wife. But this young woman was already the wife of another man, who was a great warrior.

Karambal persuaded the young woman to run away with him. When the husband found out that his wife had run away, he followed her tracks to the camp of Karambal.

In order to escape from the warrior, Karambal climbed up into a very large and tall pine tree growing near his camp. But the husband saw him hidden away among the topmost branches.

The husband gathered all the wood he could find for some distance around, and piled it in a great heap against the butt of the tree, and set fire to it.

The fire raged with great fury, burning the pine tree into cinders. The flames reached high into the air, carrying Karambal with them, and placed him in a part of the sky near the seven sisters. There he became the star called Aldebaran, in order that he might follow after the sisters, as he had done in his youth.

The Buloogan
and the Gaungun

A buloogan, a handsome young man, lived with his old uncle on the mountain called Mearrim. The buloogan told his uncle that he was going down to the coast to take part in a battle that was to be fought there.

The battle was fought on the Tweed River, and a gaungun, a young woman, saw the buloogan when he was leading his army in this battle, and fell in love with him. The buloogan saw this young woman looking at him and he took a liking to her at that moment.

Although the gaungun was promised to another man, she said that she would follow the buloogan back to the mountains. So that no one would know, the two lovers decided not to travel together, but that the buloogan should leave first and the gaungun should follow a day later.

The battle was fought over three days, and the buloogan showed that he was by far the best warrior there. After the battle the buloogan said that he was going back to Mearrim, his home, and set off early in the morning.

A day later the gaungun followed him. She camped by herself and kept a day's journey behind the buloogan. As she travelled along she was singing. The song says that she is from the seaside, and that her name is Kunbarra, and that she is going to the buloogan.

When she reached Tooloom Creek, which was the boundary of the buloogan's country, she heard the sound of someone chopping. Thinking that it was her lover, she called out, 'Where is that handsome one, where is he?'

It was the buloogan's old uncle, who was cutting grubs out of a gum tree, whom she had heard chopping. When the old uncle heard her voice, he looked down through the trees and saw the young woman. He ran towards her calling out, 'Here I am. I am your handsome one.'

When the gaungun saw this ugly old man coming down the mountain towards her, she called back to him, 'You are not my handsome one. You are an old rogue.'

Then, as the old uncle walked across the creek on a fallen tree towards her, the gaungun spoke to the tree to make it roll. The tree trunk rolled over, and the old uncle fell into the water and was drowned.

The buloogan had been out hunting. He came home to the mountains and heard the gaungun call out, 'Where is this buloogan who belongs to Mearrim?' And he answered her, 'Here! Here I am.' He went down from the mountain and she went up from the river to meet him.

The gaungun built a mia mia for herself and the buloogan. She said, 'This belongs to you and me.'

The Yams and the Kangaroos

An old man, and a young man called Biroogan, used to live together. Every day the old man would go out and gather yams which at that time used to grow on top of the ground. The old man had no trouble in getting his yams, he just had to pick them up.

Biroogan, the young man, used to go out to a place where there were plenty of wallabies and kangaroos. All these kangaroos and wallabies were blind, so that Biroogan had no trouble in getting what he wanted, and always used to bring back some for food.

Biroogan would always divide his meat with the old man, but the old fellow would give Biroogan only a small part of his yams. The two quarrelled about this and, unknown to Biroogan, the old man went to the place of the kangaroos and wallabies, and sang them, and opened their eyes.

The next day, when Biroogan went out to get some meat, he found that all the kangaroos and wallabies could see him. They at once bounded away from him. 'My kangaroos' eyes have been opened,' Biroogan said to himself. 'I'll go back to the camp and try again tomorrow.'

'What, no kangaroos?' said the old man when Biroogan got back to the camp. Biroogan just said that he had not been able to find any. He then went to lie down. 'Yes,' said the old man, 'let us lie down now. Tomorrow I'll go for some more yams, and you can get some more kangaroos.'

The next day they went out. Biroogan, without being seen, followed the old man. He saw where the old man gathered his yams, and then waited until the old man went back to the camp.

Biroogan went over to the place of the yams. He sang the yams and caused them all to go under the ground. Then he went back to the camp and told the old man what he had done.

They began to fight. But Biroogan was getting the better of the fight, and the old man ran away. At last Biroogan caught up with the old man at Yamba, where he killed him, and caused him to be turned into stone.

89

The Winking Owl

Some mothers left their children in the shade while they went hunting for honey. The children found a winking owl in a kulbadba tree. They knocked him out of the tree and chased him, shouting, 'Wa! Wa!' He sat on the ground and they caught him. They took him away to the shade, where they plucked out his feathers till he had none left. They then made fun of him.

They all spat on him. They spat down his mouth and they spat in his eyes, while he kept winking and winking. They pierced his nose and inserted a stalk of grass in it. The owl kept nodding his head. Then they threw him up into the air. 'Rise up!' they said to him. 'Fly as you used to do. We'll look at you and we'll say that you are a strong fellow.'

'Alas!' he said as he fell down again. He had no feathers. He could not fly. They threw him up again. This time he went up to the sky, while they were looking at him, till he was dim in the distance and faded from sight.

He went up to Kaluru. Kaluru is the name used by the tribes near Wyndham for Wandjina the Rain Giver. The owl was nodding all the time. 'What have you done?' said Kaluru. 'Where are your feathers?'

'The children were mocking me,' the owl said. 'They pierced my nose. They spat in my eyes. They kept throwing me up. They said, "He has no feathers! Fly!" It was a great mocking.'

Kaluru was sorry for the owl when he heard this story. He was very angry. 'I shall send the birds,' he said. 'You go,' he said to them. 'Spy them out, but leave them there.'

'Yes! Yes!' said the birds.

'Friarbird, you go first,' he said to her.

'Yes,' said the friarbird.

The friarbird found them all; the children, the men, and the mothers. But she did not bring back news of them, because she was sorry for them. The friarbird came back.

'Are the men there?' said Kaluru.

'No,' she said.

'White-gaped Honeyeater, you go,' he said to him. 'Find them, but leave them there. Come back without being seen. Do not go right up to them.'

The white-gaped honeyeater went away. He found them and returned. 'Are they there?' said Kaluru.

'No,' said the honeyeater. He had been eating wild pear and had forgotten he had seen them.

'Crow, you go,' he said to her.

'No. No. I have other things to do,' the crow said. 'I shall be eating bottle tree fruit.' Then she said, 'Yes, I will go.'

She went away. Half-way she stopped to eat bottle tree fruit. She returned. 'Are they there?' he said to her.

'No, I did not see them,' she said. She told a lie. She did not look for the men. She was eating bottle tree fruit.

'Darter Bird, you go!' he said. The darter bird went and went up to the men. It stretched out its hands. The men saw it. 'Wandjina's messenger,' they said. The darter bird returned and went up to Kaluru.

'Are the men there?' Kaluru said.

'I saw what looked like men a long way off,' the darter bird said.

'Where?'

'I did not know the place. It was dark,'it said.

'Ah! Ah!' said Kaluru. The darter bird saw them in daylight, but hid this from Kaluru.

'Goose, you go,' he said to her. 'Yes,' she said. She went up to them. They saw her. 'Goose! Goose!' they said. She returned and went up to Kaluru.

'Are the men there?' he said to her.

'No,' she said.

'Bee-eater, you go,' he said to him. He went, making a noise, clicking with his beak.

'Men! Men!' he cried. They looked, they stared, they saw him.

'It's the bee-eater,' they said.

He returned and went up to Kaluru. 'Are they there?'

'No.'

'Storm Bird, you go,' he said to her. She went up to them. 'Kuraag! Kuraag!' she cried. She was mourning for the men. She returned. She did not tell him. 'The men might all be finished,' she said in her heart. She went up to Kaluru.

'Are they there?' he said to her.

'No.'

'Man o' War Bird, you go,' he said to him. He went, but he saw the sea and he did not return, for he liked the sea. He did not go to the men. Kaluru was staring. He was worried.

'Sea-Eagle, you go,' he said to it. The sea-eagle saw the sea and went to it. He passed the men and did not return, because he liked the sea.

Kaluru was worried. 'Osprey, you go,' he said to him. Osprey went. He saw the men, but he saw the sea. He passed the men and went to the sea and did not return.

'The birds have all mocked me,' said Kaluru. 'They have not returned.' He was very angry. 'Water Goanna, you go! You birds, I will not send you any more! You never return like all those others. They all mocked me. Don't you speak to me again!'

The water goanna went. It went up to the men and returned. 'Are the men there?' he said to it. It climbed up on Kaluru's shoulder, but did not speak. 'Ah!' said Kaluru. 'Green Frog, you go,' he said to her. She went. She saw a cave, and stayed in it. She did not return. Kaluru said, 'Ah! Ah! The green frog has mocked me!' He was angry.

The owl was nodding his head. 'What is it?' said Kaluru. 'I am ashamed,' the owl said. He turned aside. He was ashamed because he had no feathers on his chest. That is why he always does that now.

Kaluru was very angry and sorry for him.

Kaluru called the side-winder lizard. It came and stood in front of Kaluru.

'You go!' he said to it. 'All the men and all the birds say that you are only rubbish. You go and try to find those men.'

'Yes,' it said. It ran, then stopped and lifted up its head. 'No,' it said. Again it ran, stopped, and in another place lifted its head. 'Here they are now!' it said, and it was glad.

'I shall kill them,' said Kaluru. He made a little cloud. The rain fell down where he was standing. The lines of falling rain were the two legs of Kaluru. The rain fell from the cloud to his head and down to his legs as he stretched out his hands.

The people covered themselves with paperbark. Kaluru threw the paperbark away from them with his hands. That was a great wind. The people ran away, but they were all gathered together by Kaluru.

'What shall we do?' they said. 'Let us go into this cave.' Then they saw Kaluru. 'Wandjina! Wandjina!' they said.

'Let us go there!' they said. Again they saw Kaluru. He kept heading them off. The earth was now boggy and they sank down. But a little wallaby hopped away. A boy and a girl said, 'Let's catch him!' They got him and clung to him. He hopped away.

Kaluru said, 'I'll head him off.' But the wallaby kept zigzagging till he got through and reached dry land. Then he threw off the children. They looked hard around. All the people were gone! All had sunk. Only the rain water was standing there. The two children went away and went to another tribe of people.

'Where are all the people?' they said to the two children. 'Kaluru made an end of them all,' they said, 'because the children made a mock of the winking owl.'

Children now do not play with the winking owl.

Where all those people sank down, the pandanus palm now stands.

The Curlew and the Owl

In ancestral times, there lived an owl who was then a man. He lived in the Narunga tribal country and owned two big dogs.

His home was in the cliffs, near the beach on the eastern side of Yorke Peninsula. Each day he went out hunting with his two dogs.

There also lived in the same place, on the beach, two curlews who were man and wife. They had several children.

One day the curlews went out to hunt, leaving their children playing at the home camp. The owl, seeing that they had gone, came down from the cliffs with his two dogs and pointing out the young curlews, said, 'There is meat for you, my dogs.' The dogs sprang forward and killed and ate the children at the camp. Finishing their meal, they went up the side of the cliffs to their cave where they all dwelt.

Back from their hunting, the two parents saw their home deserted and the remains of their children near by. After having cried and mourned for some time, they collected the remains of their children and buried them. Then the husband said to the wife, 'Never mind, I will have that man owl and his two dogs.'

So off he went into the scrub at the top of the cliffs in the direction where the owl man (or Winda) lived. In the scrub he came upon a kangaroo and speaking to it he said, 'You go and feed in front of Winda's cave, so that he can see you. He will then send a dog after you, but you will be quick and run towards and through the dense scrub. I will be hidden at a certain place, as there you will pass me.' The curlew then showed him where he would stand.

The kangaroo went out of the scrub and over to Winda's cave, where he started to feed.

The owl seeing the kangaroo, immediately ordered a dog to catch him. The dog sneaked out and up to the supposedly unsuspecting kangaroo. But it was too quick for him and went off to the densest part of the scrub, bound upon bound, with the dog chasing.

As the kangaroo bounded past the arranged place the curlew killed the dog with a club.

Thanking his friend, he went home and told his wife that he had got one dog, adding, 'I will get the other tomorrow.'

Early the next day he went out into the scrub again, and meeting the kangaroo made the same plans as on the previous day.

Seeing the kangaroo again at the entrance to the cave, the owl said to his dog, 'You had better get him.'

Again, in the same manner as before, the second dog met his death.

Thanking the kangaroo, the curlew (or Wudlaru) went home to his wife and told her the tidings, adding, 'I am now going up to kill Winda.'

Climbing the cliff again, he arrived at the entrance. Standing in front of it he called out to him to come out and fight. But the owl would not answer or come out. After waiting some time, the curlew cursed him in the following words:

'Nobody will ever like you,
You will never go out in the daytime to get food.
You will only get food at night,
You will not be able to see at any other time,
You will not be able to see the sun,
Stay there, stay there.'

So even to this day, the owl lives in caves and dark places.

The curlew then went back to his camp, on the beach, and told his wife all that had happened.

Thinking for some time, he said, 'There is nothing else for me to do.' He therefore transformed himself into the bird, curlew. His wife did likewise. To this day they still mourn their young.

The Travellers

About three-quarters of a mile north-west from the Coolangatta homestead, the home of the late Mr A. Barry, is a rock with six long grooves down its face. This rock is on the eastern side of Coolangatta Mountain, facing the sea.

The Aboriginal legend is that the grooves in this rock have been made by the feet of the spirits of the Aborigines sliding down it. The largest two grooves have been made by the men, the next two grooves by the women, and the smallest by the children.

When an Aboriginal died, his spirit went in the night to the top of this rock and, standing there for a few moments, looked out towards the sea, which is about two miles away. Then he slid down the hollow grooves, each foot resting in a groove, and when he came to the lower part of the rock, he could see the end of a very long stem of a cabbage-tree which reached from some unknown land across the sea to this rock.

He jumped on to the end of this cabbage-tree stem and walked along it to the coast, and onward across the sea. The stem continued over the sea, and, in following it, the traveller came to a place where flames of fire seemed to rise out of a hollow in the water.

If he had been a good tribesman, he would be able to pass through the flames unharmed. But if he had been a bad man, who had broken tribal laws, he might get scorched and fall into the sea, or perhaps he would get through it more or less singed.

After a while the end of the cabbage-tree stem was reached at the other side of the sea.

The traveller then continued on along a track through the bush, and after a time met a crow who said, 'You once frightened me.' The crow threw a spear at the man, but missed him, and the man kept on his way, the crow calling him bad names and making a great noise.

At another place he came to where a large fig tree was growing, and two men were there.

One of these men was standing on the ground and was some relative of the traveller. The other man who was up in the tree was an evil person and would kill him if he got the chance.

The man in the tree asks the other man to bring the traveller under the tree. The traveller's friend warns the traveller to take care. Now the man in the fig tree is gathering figs and is squeezing them together around a quartz crystal, which makes the lump of figs to increase in size and weight.

He calls to the traveller to stand in a clear space so that he can throw him the bundle of fruit. But the traveller does not trust him and will not do this. The traveller walks into a scrubby place under the tree and being hungry, stoops down to pick up some of the figs from the ground which have been shaken off by the wind.

The man in the tree then throws the bundle of figs at him, which by this time has changed into a large stone, but he misses the traveller, owing to the scrub which is in his view.

The traveller now continues on his journey and the track along which he is going passes through a rocky, narrow gorge, with scrub growing on either side. Here are some king parrots of gigantic size, who try to bite him with their strong beaks, but he holds them off with his shield and goes on through the pass. At this the parrots set up a great chattering noise.

Going further on he comes to a forest where there are plenty of trees but no under-scrub and the grass is green. There are plenty of kangaroos and other kinds of animals. Then he reaches a place where there are many Aborigines of all ages. Among them are some young men, playing ball in a clear place near the camp.

Here the traveller sees his relatives and all his friends who have died before him. He sits down a little way from the people, and when his relations see him, they come and welcome him, and take him into the camp, where they paint and dress him in the same way that he used to be when he was in his own country. After that, there is great shouting, and a corroboree, and he plays among the rest.

Presently, an old dirty-looking blackfellow, with sores on his body, comes near and calls out, 'Who came when that noise was being made just now?' The people tell him that it was only the young people playing about.

This ugly old man cannot come into the camp because there is a watercourse which marks the boundary of his hunting-grounds, beyond which he dare not pass. If he were to see the traveller he might point a bone at him or do him some other injury. This is why the people do not tell him about the traveller who has just arrived. Then the ugly old man goes back to his own camp, which is a little distance further on.

If the man who had died had been greedy or quarrelsome, or had always been causing trouble in the tribe, he would have met with a different greeting at the end of his journey.

If the traveller had been a troublesome fellow, the crow, which he first met, would have speared him. Then the crow would have picked beakfuls of flesh out of him, and knocked him about, then pulled the spear out of him, and started him off on his journey again.

When this traveller comes to the place where the big fig tree is growing, there is no friend there to warn him of danger, so he walks under the tree and begins picking up and eating the ripe figs which have fallen to the ground.

The man in the tree watches him and throws the bundles of figs, which he has changed to stone, down on the traveller, bruising him and stretching him almost lifeless on the ground. The man then comes down out of the tree and shakes the traveller, and stands him on his feet and starts him on his way, bruised and bleeding from his wounds, and scarcely able to walk.

When at last he reaches the forest of green trees and the camp of his countrymen, the people shout out to him that they don't want him there, and make signs to him to go on.

The ugly old blackfellow then calls out, 'Who came when that noise was made?' The people tell him that a stranger came. Then the old man calls the traveller to him, and takes him away to his own camp.

The wounds made by those clever, old wizards, the crow, and the man in the fig tree, never heal properly, and give this man a scabby and dirty appearance ever afterwards.

The Platypus

Djanbun is the platypus. That platypus was a man one time. He came out of Wash-pool Creek, near Yugilbar. The old people told me this story of Djanbun.

Well, this platypus-man is travelling, and he has a fire-stick in his hand. He's coming now, he's travelling from Washpool Creek to the Clarence River. He's travelling across the big mountains.

He's trying to get this fire-stick to flame like you would if you wanted to start a fire. He keeps on blowing the end of the fire-stick to make it flame, but it won't flame, and wherever the sparks fall down from the fire-stick as he blows it, they turn to gold.

Well, this platypus-man, his mouth started to get wide from blowing on the fire-stick. We used to blow on the fire-stick when we were young, and my mother used to say to us, 'Don't blow the fire-stick like that, or you'll be like Djanbun and turn into a platypus.'

Well, when Djanbun gets down to the Clarence River, he feels that he has a big mouth from blowing on the fire-stick. Then he starts to wonder, 'What am I going to do here now?' He had got tired of blowing on the fire-stick to make it flame, so he throws the fire-stick down.

Then he thinks to himself, 'Well, the best thing for me to do now is to jump in the water.' So he jumps into the Clarence River. And as soon as he jumps into the water he turns into a platypus. That's him, that's Djanbun now. Well, he was a man one time.

Now Billy Charlie, he found this nugget of gold at the place where Djanbun jumped into the water. When I heard about this, I thought, 'Well now, that must have been the djangurr, the fire-stick, that he found.' Because Billy Charlie found that gold right where the fire-stick was thrown down.

Well, he put the nugget in an old stocking he had, and he's coming along carrying it back to his blady-grass camp. When he gets near to the camp, his sister, who was sitting down, calls out, 'Brother, what's that you've got in the stocking?'

Billy says, 'Ngarbarr.' That means, 'Have a look.' His sister got the stocking and emptied it out, and there was a big nugget of gold.

And she got excited and said, 'O brother, you'd better give me a little bit.' So they put the nugget on a log, and Billy Charlie cut it with an axe and gave her a piece.

The old people told me this story of Djanbun, and they showed me the way Djanbun went. He came out of Washpool Creek and travelled over the big range, and then went into the Clarence River.

The Flowering Tea-Tree

One time I was camped near the grave of an old native of our tribe. The grave was on the side of a hill, and I noticed this tea-tree coming into flower there. It was growing out of the head of the grave of this old native.

I thought that somebody must have planted it there, so I asked the old Kummi, that means Queen, of our people about it. This old lady, she lived to be 111 years old. She called me her grandson, and she starts to tell me the story now.

This old native, who was buried in that grave, was the boss of all the fishes in the river. Those deep waterholes in the river were his jurraveel, that means that they belonged to him.

Well, the other Aborigines knew about this, so, whenever they wanted fish, they knew that they must go to this certain man who owned them. They'd go and ask him, 'Could we have some of the fishes today that we want?'

And this old feller who owned the fishes would say, 'Yes, come along with me and I'll show you where to catch them.'

And there's a lot of tea-trees along the river that grow right over these deep waterholes. And this old feller, he'd always go out on these tea-trees and have a look in the waterholes to see where the fish was.

And he'd say to the fellers who wanted the fish, 'Set your net in a certain place there.' This net was called 'mundung'. It belonged to the old people. They'd make it out of bark, or reeds.

Then this old feller would say, 'Now get the boys to come up here and jump in the water and splash and make the fishes come into the net.'

This old feller would tell the boys how to splash the water, but he'd never move away from the tea-tree limb he was standing on. Once they'd pushed the fish into the net, there would be enough for everyone. A certain length of the river was this old feller's jurraveel.

Then this old feller died. Then they buried him. It must have been years after he died that I saw this little tea-tree come into blossom on the grave of this old man.

This old Queen, who told me the story, she said to me, 'You know why that tree grew on that old feller's head? Because he always used to stand on that tea-tree and look for the fish. Nobody grew that tree. It grew itself.'

I always used to call this old lady Kummi, that means Queen. And she used to call me Kummi, too, and that means grandson. That's our way of talking Bunjalung. That old lady was a Queen, and that's how I come to know this story.

The Kangaroo-Man

One time my grandfather and grandmother and their tribe were travelling from Nowra to Currambene Creek. When they came to Falls Creek, they saw some black-fellows who were 'bugeens', clever blackfellows. But my grandfather's tribe travelled on and made their camp at Bit-Bit Creek. My grandfather called out to the tribe, 'Make your camps, kabookas, and fires all round this place.'

That evening they went out hunting after kangaroos. Kangaroos come out feeding near sunset, you know. They see an old-man kangaroo sitting up. My grandfather sings out to an old man who had a muzzle-loader, 'Go on, give it to him!' The old man takes aim, fires: Boo-oom!

When the smoke clears away that kangaroo is still sitting there. Grandfather sings out, 'Go on, old man. Give it to him again.' The old man rams down more powder and shot into the barrel of the muzzle-loader. He takes aim, fires: Boo-oom! The barrel of that muzzle-loader splits open.

Grandfather calls out, 'Walthow. Come on. We'd better go on back to the camp.'

When they get near to the camp, my grandmother calls out, 'Get any kangaroos?'

'No,' grandfather says, 'those kangaroos were all bugeens.' He tells the old lady about the gun barrel splitting open.

'Right-oh, boys,' my grandfather sings out, 'tell all the old people to make up good fires and pile on plenty of logs.'

The tribe make their beds and spread out their bejahs, these are wallaby-skin and possum rugs sewn with kangaroo sinews. They sit down and give one another a smoke of garndee, which is tobacco.

Now the bugeen, the clever blackfellow who had changed himself into that old-man kangaroo, had gone down to the river and picked up some little white stones. Then he'd come up from the river and climbed up a big woollybutt tree. High up in the tree he was stretched out along a limb like a goanna.

At the foot of this tree the old people were sitting round a fire. The bugeen drops one of his pebbles down into the ashes. The old people don't take any notice. Another stone comes down and scatters the coals of the fire.

'Ngut! Look out!' my grandfather sings out. He looks up into the big tree. 'Come on you boys.' He sings out. 'Get bushes and logs. Make up a big fire here.'

Soon a big fire is going. Blackfellows scatter around and look up into the tree. 'What's up there?' some of them ask. 'That looks like a big bough up there,' others call.

Up in the tree, the bugeen has bent leaves and branches round and over him. But the tribe, looking up, see his side in the firelight. They aim another muzzle-loader at him. 'Go on, give it to him,' they shout. Boo-oom!

The bugeen is still there. He hasn't moved. 'Go on, give it to him again.' Boo-oom!

The big fire is leaping and flaring up into the tree. They see him now. Drops of blood fall on to the bushes.

They see the bugeen, lit up by the fire, lying along the limb like a goanna. Then, like a gale of wind, whee-eesh, whoo-oo, he's gone. He flies away into the night and goes into some caves at the Shoalhaven River.

Later on, two old men were out looking for koala bears, honey, goannas, or anything they could find. The two old men see this bugeen in a cave.

That cave is up in a cliff face. That cliff's a dangerous place. One slip and you're gone. You couldn't get to that cave by swimming and then trying to climb up the cliff face. Those two old men go home and tell my grandfather. 'We couldn't get over to that cave, but we saw him,' they say.

My grandfather says, 'That's right, we shot him. That's him. He's the bugeen all right.'

The Maker of Boomerangs

Adam Cooper was the cleverest blackfellow God put on this earth. He used to make boomerangs. He'd call up a boy to go with him.

He'd get his stone tomahawk and cut out a circle in the ground. In this circle he'd put stringybark. Then he'd throw his boomerang and make it spin, hovering in the air, over the bark. Out of that stringybark smoke would start to rise. The stringybark would catch alight. That's how this blackfellow could make fire.

He'd send that boomerang away. It would go far away and fall on the ground. He'd make that boomerang roll. He'd clap his hands and the boomerang would travel back to him along the ground.

He'd make a good fire and let it burn down to glowing coals. Then he'd corroboree on the coals and there wouldn't be a mark to show on his feet.

He had a white stone. He had it planted. He wouldn't tell anyone where he kept it hidden. He used to sing this stone in the language. He would sing this stone and make it rain, and rain heavy.

Adam Cooper's tribe used to make nets out of rushes. They would stretch the nets across a big creek to stop the ducks coming down. Then they'd go up to the top of the creek and hunt the ducks down. They'd throw their boomerangs whistling in the air over the ducks to drive them down into the nets. Those ducks, flying low over the water, would hit the net and break their necks.

That's the truth. That's the finish. That's the way they did it in the old times. I've seen it done myself.

The Porcupine Ejenak

This little porcupine Ejenak whistles a little song when he's travelling. He goes along. Perhaps he goes down to the river to have a drink of water. He walks around the beach listening all the time for anyone walking. If anyone is about he hears the sand squeak.

He goes in the water, and walks underneath the water looking for his food. He comes out on the other side and walks about.

He comes to a bulldog-ant's nest. He pokes his little claws into the nest and bulldog-ants come out. He pokes out his little tongue and licks them up and gets his tucker.

The Wild Women

Old Jimmy Clemens was a clever old man. He was travelling once to Moss Vale. At Fitzroy Falls, as he was walking along the track, he heard some wild women. He heard them laughing. There was a tribe of them. He heard them talking.

Once when old Jimmy was in his hut he heard one of these wild women coming. He heard her calling to him from outside in the darkness. She threw little pebbles on to the roof. She knew his name and called out, 'You there, Jimmy? Jimmy, you there?'

She pushed the door open but old Jimmy pulled his tomahawk out from behind his neck and slung it at her. The tomahawk hit the door-post and stuck in there.

Old Jimmy chased her away into the bush. But the wild woman was too clever. She could turn into a mist, or a wallaby doe. Old Jimmy chased her and chased her but she got away from him into some caves.

Old Jimmy was clever too. He could feel when they were near. Those wild women want you for a husband. They take you away into the bush and the mountains for six months. They make you stupid. You can't hear anything. There's always six of them. They come down to Currumbene Creek near Huskisson.

You hear them coming. You hear them laughing and talking. They know your name and call out to you. You mustn't answer. If you answer, you go stupid. You know nothing until they get you to their cave. You can't get away. They feed you. Might be you have a bit of honey, possum, goanna, or mushroom.

When they let you go they say, 'After three weeks I come for you.' You can't hide. Wherever you go they find you.

You say, 'I'll get away somewhere.' But it's no good. You can't get away from those wild women.

Old Jimmy Clemens was very clever. He was the only man to break their power. Those wild women are very good to look at. They have long hair.

The Wild
Cherry Tree

This wild cherry tree, it makes a good shade. I lie down under it and go to sleep. By and by I hear a big roaring sound. 'Oh, a thunder storm is coming up, I'll soon fix that.'

I break a branch off this tree and burn it. The smoke goes straight up into the sky. Those big rolling clouds divide. One cloud goes one way, one cloud goes the other way. You hear thunder crashing, rolling away down the sky.

This is my tree. This is our sacred tree. It belongs to all the blackfellows. You, too, you're a bit of a blackfellow, you try it. You'll say, 'That's true what old Billy Bamboo says.' It's true all right. That's our old jungle king.

Well, my tribe got shot up. One white man found a baby near the camp. He took the baby back to the station on his horse. That baby grew up to be my father.

A Victorian tribe came and fought with the Wallaga Lake tribe. An old man and his wife were running away along a pad. They were carrying a baby with them. Men with spears were hard behind them. Those two with the baby come to a bend in the track. They see a big log hollowed out by fire. They put the baby inside the log and run on. The Victorian tribe catch them up and kill them.

The white man was riding his horse along. He hears a baby crying in the bush. He looks all about, comes to the big log and listens. He kneels at the log and listens. He goes to one end and sees the pale feet of the baby sticking out. He takes the child and rears it up and gives it his name. And that baby was my mother.

Over in the sandhills are the bones of the tribe who were killed.

Me? I'm Billy Bamboo. Anyone will tell you. The buck-jump rider. The bare-knuckle fighter. We used to stand toe to toe and fight. We'd go down to the creek and wash the blood off our faces and come back and into it again. I was a flash young feller, in jodhpurs, riding-boots, shirt and hat.

No, I can't see now as well as I used to. And I have to use this stick now. Yes, I've heard those hairy-men, the 'doolagarls', in the mountains, round our camp. You should have seen those old people. They could have told you all about 'bugeens', and 'gooins', and 'doolagarls'. All those old people are gone from this mission. They're all ghosts, spirits in this place.

The Gold
of Billy Bulloo

Old Billy Bulloo was a clever old man.

He would never go out fishing on a calm day. But if the sea was rough, mountains high, he would jump in his canoe and get his fish by spearing them. He could see the fish in the waves.

A mullet, he never travels in the calm. He waits for the wind to blow a gale. Soon as ever he feels that wind on him—cold—he jumps out of the water. He's feeling for that westerly wind. When that wind blows, you see the water black with leaping mullet, thousands and thousands of leaping mullet.

That's when old Billy Bulloo used to get his fish.

Old Billy Bulloo used to travel across country to the Burragorang Valley tribe. He found the gold on the Shoalhaven. He used to come down with enough to get tucker for four or five weeks. He would go to the publican in Nowra and trade his gold for tucker or a bottle of rum.

Lots of white men tried to find out where he got the gold. They used to follow him up, but when he got to the bush, he would lose them. They never found out where he got the gold.

The last one he told was my old granny. While she was in her health and strength she wanted to take us out and show us where it was.

But you know what young fellows are, they're here today, and gone tomorrow.

Under the She-oaks

Every time I lie down alongside a river and hear the wind in those oaks it puts me in mind of my poor old grand-uncle Minah.

My old grand-uncle was lying down under the oaks and he was dying. My old dad was with him, looking after him.

When I'm lying down under those oaks down at Bega, I used to think about old uncle Minah. He used to put his arms round me and say, 'My great-great-grandchildren.'

I was his favourite. I was like a little poddy-calf, a little fat-belly feller, you might say. I was never with the young fellers. I followed the old people. They would hunt me back. I would cry and they would take me up and put me on their shoulders. I used to sit down and listen to the old people yarning.

Whenever I used to see one of those old fellers going off with a spear for marrung, fish, I'd watch him. Away I'd go. I'd run after him.

He'd look round quick. 'You naughty boy,' he'd say, 'why don't you go home? You'll frighten all the fish.'

I'd chuck myself down and into it, whingeing and howling.

'All right,' the old lad would say, 'come on. Don't you make a noise. We're going to sneak on the marrung.'

The old lad would crouch right down with his fish-spear. He'd make a feint move to frighten the fish. When the fish didn't move he'd drive the spear right into him. He'd have that fish shaking on his spear.

I was only a little feller, but I had that sense to follow and learn how to do all those things. That's why I don't use a line for my fish. I use my fish-spear. My father taught me how to make them. I can use the womerah and the spear with two barbs. I can make a boomerang to go whistling like a duck, and come back, right back to my foot.

Every time I come to a river like this and hear the wind in those she-oaks, I sit down and those times come back to me. I can see my old great-uncle Minah lying down. He had a long white smoky beard, walloo, we call it, and his hair, jirral, was smoke-dried, white.

He was lying down and looking up at the sky, and must have been saying in his own language, 'I'm leaving all my little grandchildren. I'm leaving them.'

Nagacork's Goodbye

And the old man Nagacork went on a long walkabout to see all the tribesmen, the birds, animals, fish and reptiles.

And as Nagacork travelled through all the different countries of the tribes he sang:

'Allo, allo, allo, allo, allo, cha nallah, wirrit, burra burra, cubrimilla, cubrimilla. Bo bo.' This means, 'Oh well, all you people who belong to me, you have changed into men, animals, birds, reptiles, fish, sun, moon and stars. I go now. I go forever. You will see me no more. But all the time I will watch about you.'

And the tribesmen say that they can see the old man Nagacork lying among the stars. His lubra is lying near him with one arm behind her head. And the tribesmen say that the stream of stars that the white man calls the Milky Way is the smoke of Nagacork's campfire drifting across the night.

Glossary

Bandicoot: Small marsupial animal

Barn-yun-bee: Totem of person, bird, animal, etc.

Barramundi: Large fish, found in fresh water and salt water

Billabong: Deep and wide part of river, lagoon, waterhole

Brolga: Native companion, Australian crane, dancing bird

Bugeen: Evil spirit in form of totem

Bunyip: Legendary animal

Byama: Aborigines' God, Father of all

Coolamon: Wooden vessel used for carrying water, food, or small child

Corroboree: Big dance

Damper: Type of bread, cooked in coals on a camp fire

Dilly-bag: Woven fibre bag used for carrying food, belongings

Dingo: Wild dog

Diprotodon: Extinct, large animal, inhabited swamps in central Australia

Doolagarl: Huge, ape-like, hairy man

Doonoots: Owls, mopokes

Dreamtime: In the Beginning, Creation time

Drone-pipe: Hollow length of bamboo, tree branch used as wind instrument

Fire stick: Stick with one end burning

Garndee: Native name for tobacco

Goanna: Lizard, runs very fast and can climb trees

Gunnai: Women's digging stick

Honey ants: Ants which store honey in their bodies

Jabiru: Tall swamp bird, like a stork

Jodhpurs: Stockman's riding trousers

Kabookas: Camps

Kanake: Club

Kurri: Aboriginal

Lily-bulbs: Bulbs eaten for food

Maccassars: Voyagers from Malay

Mia-mia: Shelter, hut, made of bark, branches or grass

Mopoke: Boobook owl

Muzzle-loader: Old type of gun

Native bear: Koala bear

Nullah nullah: Club

Paperbark tree: Tree with loose bark that looks like paper

Perentie: Large desert goanna

Point a bone: Place a curse on an enemy, to kill him

Possum: Opossum, small marsupial animal, lives in trees

Rainbow-Snake: Huge, legendary snake

Roly-poly: Round bush-like plant of the plains

Sing: Make magic song

Song sticks: Two sticks for beating time, accompaniment to song, corroboree

Sugar-bag: Native honey in comb

Tjarada: Love song

Tjarmo: Roots which contain poison

Totem: Bird, animal, etc., which is person's spirit form

Tucker: Food

Uli-tarra: Aborigines' God

Waddy: Club

Walkabout: Long journey

Wandjina: Rain God

Wirreenun: Clever man, wizard

Womerah: Piece of wood used for throwing spears

Yabber: Talk

Yam: Tuber, edible bulb

Yela: Father